Praise for *Trauma Alchemy*

"Hearing people from all around the globe work through their struggles and use SBY as an outlet and source of light is what fuels me to keep going. Keep finding my peace. Keep fighting for me. It's a comfort to know I'm not alone in my struggles."

—**Jen B.,** SBY Community Member

"I suffered from severe arthritis flare ups. My back was constantly killing me and I had anxiety over the words working out. I thought very poorly of myself and participated in a lot of negative self talk. Telling myself I was too lazy to put on shoes in the morning to be active. I carried the weight of multiple people on my body so it was hard for me to want to do anything active. I had started using SBY free youtube videos for a few weeks and had noticed my back hurt much less and I was able to be more mobile each and every day that I kept going with my lifestyle change. I knew I could commit to at least 10 min of yoga a day and that became my non-negotiable. As I got stronger I wanted to do more and have more video options to choose from."

—**Meghan S.,** SBY Community Member and Lifestyle Coach and Founder of See Meghan Shrink

"The SBY community empowered me to overcome the impulse to isolate myself by engaging with fellow SBYogis. The membership empowered me to overcome limiting beliefs by providing full length classes that I can comfortably complete. Now I show up for myself and give myself what I need to fill my cup. The membership has given me an arsenal of positive affirmations and education to accompany the lifestyle that SBY has modeled."

—**Bryan P.,** SBY Community Member

D1452950

"I struggled with consistency and having the calendar(s) and seeing the modifications made me feel comfortable. I wasn't trying to be a perfect yogi and Sarah Beth reminds me that it's a practice that encourages me to keep doing it."

—**Jen H.M.**, SBY Community Member

"Before SBY, I was in weekly therapy sessions with a psychiatrist, for PTSD, depression, anxiety, and suicidal ideation, after losing my son, Nick, to suicide... I was not in a good place. After years of intense psychotherapy, I felt "talked out," I had nothing left to say, but I knew I still needed something more... something to heal me from the inside out.

I found SBY on YouTube, and was instantly hooked, I felt so good!! After doing those videos for months, I decided to get the membership, as I felt ready for longer, more intense workouts. Every day, no matter how I felt, I made my way to my mat, six days per week. I took all my sadness, grief, and anger to my mat with me, and the more emotions I felt, the harder I worked... it became my new therapy session I guess you could say.

My life has changed immensely since I joined the SBY Tribe & Membership. I feel the best mentally, physically, and spiritually that I have in years. I also love that no matter what kind of day you're having, you can get total support from Sarah Beth and our Tribe... we're always there for each other.

Getting the SBY Membership is the best thing I ever could have done for myself. This may sound dramatic, but for years, after losing my son, I prayed for death... for real. But deep down, I knew my son would not want that for me. Since joining SBY, I get up every morning, excited for what the day may bring, and always anxious to hit my mat!! My boy would be so proud!!!"

—**Laurie T.**, SBY Community Member

"Shortly before starting SBY, I had just quit a job that was extremely demanding and absorbed all my energy. I was feeling unhealthy in body and mind as all the choices I was making at the time were stress-related. Bad food habits. Looking at myself in the mirror & frustrated by how I had allowed myself to "let go" and put on so much extra weight. I was extremely uncomfortable and extremely irritable.

After leaving a highly stress-related job, I turned my focus on myself. I had to return to the healthy version of myself again, both mentally and physically. I joined a community of women online where we shared workouts every day, healthy recipes and motivation. One of my friends in this community (Jen) asked me if I had heard of Sarah Beth Yoga. She had just found her on YouTube and suggested I try her 7Day Yoga Challenge. In fact, we started the challenge together & checked in with each other every day! We shared our experiences of how SBY made us feel empowered, strong, yet calm and focused for the rest of our day! We took this to our social media platforms and I recall emailing links to everyone I know! :)

When the SBY app launched, there was no hesitation. I knew I wanted to be a part of this Membership & Community for life!"

—**Carlynn R.**, SBY Community Member

"The reason I started SBY was because I was having hip pain so bad I couldn't really walk. I went and got it checked and it turns out I have some kind of bone deformity and the only way they said to treat it was regular injections until a hip replacement was necessary. I'm really into as much stuff in my life being natural as I can, and also I'm only in my mid-30s I'm not trying to sign up for all that yet, so I made a deal with myself - I'd do yoga every single day for a month and if the pain lessened I'd continue that, and if I still couldn't walk I'd put my head down and start with the injections.

I found SBY on YouTube, and here I am almost two years later and I still have yet to start the injections. I'm back to running a couple times a week and my pain is gone.

—**Val M.**, SBY Community Member

"I found Sarah Beth Yoga on YouTube during a time when I was suffering from pretty severe lower back pain and was desperate to find something that would help. I had been seeing a chiropractor which helped some but the thought of going to a doctor and being put on pain medication or surgery just wasn't something I was ready to take on yet. I'm a true beginner and have never done yoga in my life. I was hooked by the first video. YouTube is great but the SBY app/FB community really provides so much more information, guidance, and support. My back pain, by the way, has lessened so much and does not inhibit my life any longer."

—**Ashley R.**, SBY Community Member

TRAUMA
ALCHEMY

TRAUMA ALCHEMY

TRANSFORM HARDSHIP,
STRESS, AND TRAUMA
INTO **YOUR BEST LIFE**
THROUGH YOGA

Sarah Beth Yoga
@sarahbethyoga

Trauma Alchemy copyright © 2023 by Sarah Beth Yoga

Sarah Beth Yoga LLC
P.O. Box 631594
Highlands Ranch, CO 80163
www.sarahbethyoga.com
Send feedback to book@sarahbethyoga.com

Publisher's Cataloging-in-Publication
(Provided by Cassidy Cataloguing Services, Inc.).
    Names: Sarah Beth Yoga, author.
    Title: Trauma alchemy : transform hardship, stress, and trauma into your best life
        through yoga /
    Sarah Beth Yoga.
    Description: Highlands Ranch, CO : Sarah Beth Yoga LLC, [2023]
    Identifiers: ISBN: 979-8-9876242-0-3 (hardcover) | 979-8-9876242-1-0
        (softcover) |
    979-8-9876242-2-7 (ebook) | 979-8-9876242-3-4 (audiobook)
    Subjects: LCSH: Yoga--Psychological aspects. | Psychic trauma--Exercise ther-
        apy. | Stress management.
    | Emotions--Health aspects.
    Classification: LCC: RA781.67 .T73 2023 | DDC: 613.7046--dc23

This book is dedicated to you, dear reader.

You are about to begin a transformational journey. One of awareness, acceptance, forgiveness and ultimately... healing. Like your first ever yoga experience it may feel awkward and unfamiliar at first, but trust that with time and practice you'll shed the layers of who you are not so that you can shine brightly for who you truly are and live the life you were meant to live.

You're ready for this.

Contents

Tell Me What You Think

Let other readers know what you thought of *Trauma Alchemy*. Please write an honest review for this book on your favorite online bookshop.

★ ★ ★ ★ ★

The Trauma Yoga Collection and Calendar

The chapters outlined in this book have been turned into individual yoga sessions so you can supplement the work you're doing here with your yoga practice. You'll practice the strategies and techniques in real time with the poses and sequences that align so you can physically embody your healing journey.

The eight-week Trauma Yoga Calendar guides you through each chapter, along with yoga practices that will give you space to contemplate and process what you've read and what it means to you. This allows you to take your time as you work through each chapter. In the end, you can revisit any specific step of your trauma alchemy by either rereading the chapter, practicing that step's yoga video again, or both.

You can access the Trauma Yoga Collection and Calendar through the SarahBethYoga Membership + App. Go to https://www.sarahbethyoga.com/traumacalendar or scan the QR code above with your phone to learn more.

CHAPTER 1

YOGA OFF THE MAT

Hi, yogi!
Let me ask you . . .

Why do *you* do yoga?

Maybe you'll say, "To manage stress," "To stay active," or "To relieve anxiety or depression."

Maybe your stress level increased recently because you just started a new job, or moved to a new city, or had a baby, and you're overwhelmed with everything you need to do. Some people do yoga to relieve stress or pain, like chronic neck and shoulder tension, back pain, or stress-related headaches. Other people do yoga to increase mobility, strength, or overall flexibility.

Regardless of what brought you to yoga in the first place, I'm sure you got from it what everyone does—immediate relief. So you keep doing it. Just the deep breathing helps you feel calm and alleviates mental overstimulation. Combine that with the physical movement of yoga, and you feel more present. Lighter.

But it's not just about *why* you do yoga. What happens after the session is over?

You feel bliss. Gratitude. You step outside, and suddenly all the colors of nature seem more vibrant. You feel so good, you know you want to do it again.

Like many others, you probably started yoga for the physical benefits, but you continue to do it because you've seen your life improve. You spend time taking care of yourself, and after a while, you find self-awareness and presence and peace.

So you practice yoga. You keep doing it because it makes you feel good . . . but you may not really know why, besides the deep breaths, long stretches, and workout endorphins, of course.

Beyond the physical benefits, there's something deeper that keeps calling you back to your mat. Gradually, over time, something physical *and* mental has shifted in you. Perhaps others have noticed the changes in you, too.

This shift happens each time we practice yoga. The secret is that the sequence of a yoga practice—the poses, flows, and stretches, and the lessons taught, like awareness, compassion, and focus—metaphorically represent the stages of moving from trauma . . . to transformation . . . to release.

And it's this exact secret that I will outline for you in the chapters of this book so you can transform your stress, hardships, and trauma into your best life through yoga, on and off your mat.

You may not think of yourself as someone who has experienced trauma, but most people have. According to the American Psychological Association:

> Trauma is an emotional response to a terrible event like an accident, assault, or natural disaster. Immediately after the event, shock and denial are typical. Longer-term reactions include unpredictable emotions, flashbacks, strained relationships, and even physical symptoms like headaches or nausea.[1]

If that doesn't resonate with you, you may find your story in a specific category of trauma—acute, chronic, or complex:

---

1 - "Trauma," American Psychological Association, updated August 2022, https://www.apa.org/topics/trauma.

1. Acute trauma results from a single incident.
2. Chronic trauma is repeated and prolonged such as domestic violence or abuse.
3. Complex trauma is exposure to varied and multiple traumatic events, often of an invasive, interpersonal nature.[2]

Most people we interact with every day of our lives have endured one type of trauma or another. I didn't know I had suppressed trauma until I was diagnosed with complex post-traumatic stress disorder (CPTSD) from complex trauma, as listed above. And so began my trauma alchemy journey that has resulted in me living my best life today. But we'll get into that later . . .

Like me, the symptoms of trauma you've experienced are what likely brought you to the mat in the first place. The anxiety, depression, stress, tightness in your chest, neck, or shoulders . . . Little did you know that yoga not only relieves those symptoms but, with a mindful approach, can also help you heal the wounds that caused them.

People do this every day in their practice without realizing it. They are just scratching the surface of yoga's transformative and healing nature. *Trauma Alchemy: Transform Hardship, Stress, and Trauma into Your Best Life through Yoga* is an opportunity to see what lies beneath—and to think deeper about how yoga can transform how you live your life and how you feel through your self-talk, self-confidence, and self-awareness.

This book unveils the mystery of what yoga does for you so those good feelings last both on and off the mat. It allows you to utilize yoga's benefits to soften the hard moments in life. It's an opportunity to process and heal trauma, stresses, and hardships using the tools of your yoga practice with me as your guide.

---

2 - "Trauma-informed Care," Missouri's Early Care & Education Connections, accessed TK, https://earlyconnections.mo.gov/professionals/trauma-informed-care.

My Yoga Story

I went to my first yoga class when I was fifteen and a half years old. In addition to being in the depths of raging hormones, my life was difficult. I had just emerged from a decade of challenges—childhood trauma, a significant death, serious illness, family court—and as a result, my family's relationships had exploded. I was also in a severely abusive romantic relationship. I knew well enough to wear waterproof mascara because I cried every day.

With my driving permit, I drove myself to a free yoga class at a high-end gym. To say I felt out of place and ill-prepared is an understatement. The experience was humbling and embarrassing, but I did my best even though I was essentially a baby giraffe in a room full of flexible gazelles. As I drove home afterward, I realized I felt . . . good. I was a gangly teenage girl, depressed and high-strung about my situation in life, and yet in that moment, I felt calm. Grounded. I knew for sure that I needed more of that in my life. But why I suddenly felt that way was a mystery to me.

For the next few years, I went to yoga classes on and off. I still felt humbled and not at all like those other impressive, acrobatic yogis. But I knew I needed it.

Yoga is often taught superficially. People feel good afterward, but they don't know why, and most don't know the depth of the practice beyond the poses or what half the words and terminology mean. And there's not enough time in a single class to teach all this. Yoga used to be taught one-on-one so the student could learn better, but now it's taught in studios with thirty attendees with a different teacher every class and different students every time.

When I was just shy of twenty-one, I decided to quit the on-and-off modeling job I had landed as a teenager. I also wanted to stop moonlighting as an exotic dancer. I had tens of thousands of dollars in student loan debt that my part-time retail job didn't cover, much less basic necessities and living expenses. I had been able to earn some money off my looks and reduce the debt, but I had reached the point where I was just done with both jobs. I wanted to pursue a profession that wasn't a competition of age and beauty.

I lived off my savings for a month while I tried to figure out my next move. One day, I told my boyfriend (and now husband), Leland, "I know—I can be a barista!" The fact that I said "barista" as my dream job after thinking that hard about it tells you I didn't have a lot of options. Or at least, I thought I didn't. We all need coffee, of course, and for that, we have baristas to thank. But the barista life really wasn't my biggest dream.

"I think you can dream a little bigger," Leland responded. "If money was no object, what would you *want* to do?"

He had recently given me copies of the personal development classics *The 4-Hour Workweek: Escape 9–5, Live Anywhere, and Join the New Rich* and *Rich Dad, Poor Dad: What the Rich Teach Their Kids about Money That the Poor and Middle Class Do Not!*, opening my eyes to the wonderful world of entrepreneurship. The idea of dreaming bigger was already planted. So I started a YouTube channel called the Sarah-BethShow because . . . what else would I call it? And where else would I create content back in 2010 other than YouTube? I didn't know what it would be besides my life and whatever I was into at the time. (Leland and I had recorded a few videos of our experiments with the raw food diet, for example.)

The week after I published my first YouTube video, I noticed a poster for yoga teacher training at the yoga studio I had been going to. Of course, that insecure teenager inside me thought, *Who am I to teach yoga?* I shot myself down, but Leland picked me back up. "You won't know until you try," he said. So I took the rest of my savings and signed up. Yoga had certainly helped me feel good. Maybe I could help other people feel good, too.

After I got certified, I got a few jobs teaching yoga in gyms and in studios. Then, with the help of a friend who was leasing a banquet hall, I launched my own donation-based class called OMroom. Teaching those classes showed me I could teach yoga my way, and anybody, regardless of their finances, could attend. I wasn't just teaching yoga—I was building a community with self-healing-themed classes.

After several months, the banquet hall I was using to teach OMroom became unavailable. I had to transition, so I started recording yoga videos for my YouTube channel and changed the name to SarahBethYoga. It was the same as OMroom but online. Now anyone could do my yoga for free, and I still got to teach it my way.

With years of modeling under my belt, I was already good at reading scripts and looking right at the camera. Now I also know how to teach yoga. I learned about production and what looked best on video. I was already familiar with manipulating my voice for voice overs because I used to sing in a choir. Little by little, all these pieces of me came together so perfectly. But I was afraid to commit to the business of a YouTube channel. I was afraid to make it more than a hobby. What if it failed?

I can tell you, twelve years later, it did not fail. Over those years, my YouTube channel turned from hobby to business. And the consistent support from yogis all around the world now provides for my family and my team, and has helped us donate more than $60,000 to fight human sex trafficking. At the time of this writing, the SarahBethYoga YouTube channel is closing in on 1.6 million subscribers from all over the globe!

In the early years, I recorded themed sequences like I had done in the studio and slowly built an audience. I focused on my subscribers. What did they want? What did they need? I learned about business and internet marketing. I was finding myself and building my portfolio of skills. I moved from my home state of Minnesota to Colorado, my new home, and got a job as a chiropractic assistant. This sparked my interest in functional movement and mobility. After about a year working as a chiropractic assistant, the time came for me to quit that job and turn my YouTube channel side hustle into a full-time business. I've since created more than seven hundred yoga videos and launched SarahBethYoga Membership + App, where I work directly with my private member community to host monthly yoga calendars, provide exclusive content, and speak in depth about the self-healing aspects of yoga. My focus is, and always has been, on making yoga easy to follow so you can move its benefits off your mat and into your day-to-day life.

Because I have a larger sample size than most people who teach yoga, I can see that the same blissful effect it had on me is also affecting my students. How yoga worked for me, it works for others—and I've discovered why.

What brought you to yoga in the first place may have been the consequences of trauma—physical, mental, emotional. And your time on the mat is often the only time during the week when you spend time on yourself and you feel better. It transforms the stresses of everyday life, the heavy memories of what happened in your past that you're carrying in your body, and turns it into something beautiful that serves you.

Heavy memories *feel* like a physical weight that you carry both in your body and in your mind. And what repeatedly shows up in your mind manifests in your body. But this weight doesn't have to be something that drags you down, pulling you into exhaustion. Instead, it can be a weight you intentionally pick up and use to become stronger. Eventually, the weight is not what drags you down—it's what transforms you. Instead of being an obstacle to growth that keeps you in pain, it pushes you to see your problems and confront them. Through your yoga practice, you let the weight of trauma release its hold on you. The solution is to carry the weight until it's no longer heavy and no longer a weight. It doesn't own you; you own it. You have the control.

Yoga realigns you, opening you up both internally and externally. When you do the work, the healing happens on its own. Healing is a natural progression and result of each practice.

When I started doing yoga as a teenager, things like trauma weren't spoken about the way they are now. There were people writing books about it, but it wasn't a mainstream conversation. While it's helpful to raise awareness, it can also halt people's growth. You can get trapped in a state of victimhood, encouraged to identify with your trauma. But it is not who you are, and that's not what this book is about.

Yet most of us have experienced trauma significant enough to leave its mark one way or another. The trick is to not treat it like you're trapped with it. Don't make it an extension of yourself—become aware of it as an experience you had that, ultimately, you can learn and grow from.

For many people, trauma is what breaks *and* builds them. Sometimes traumas are what drive us and make us the person we are today. And when we've done the work to heal from it, we give others around us permission to do the same. Would I be where I am, writing to you, had I not experienced the trauma I did? It's not that I'm happy about it—nobody wants to suffer enough that it leaves scars. But pain is often the greatest teacher of lessons and spurs life-changing transformations.

I call this trauma alchemy.

Trauma Alchemy: Rewriting the Past

Merriam-Webster's definition of alchemy is "a power or process that changes or transforms something in a mysterious or impressive way."

Alchemy is transformation—changing one thing into another. Trauma alchemy is changing what drains you into something that fills you up. Leland says that I'm an alchemist in the best way—I can take any bad situation and make it beautiful.

In the transition from YouTube as a side hustle to a full-time gig, the launch of the SarahBethYoga App bombed. The day it was supposed to go live . . . it couldn't. Not ready, too many bugs, etcetera. I had to come clean with subscribers. I admitted it wasn't ready. I thought postponing the release was going to be a disaster, but the delay only increased the hype and showed my transparency. We eventually launched with a larger membership base than we could have imagined. Sometimes your plans fall through, but when you surrender to the universe, they fall into a new pattern.

When I was eight years old, I was diagnosed with ulcerative colitis. There's no known cause for this autoimmune disease that affects the colon. It results in flare-ups and remissions, and the colon can develop ulcers during flare-ups with mucous, diarrhea, and blood. This means I've been bedridden and toilet-ridden many times before, and likely will be again. I could be depressed about it and let it take over my life. But I've been living with it for so long I see it now as an early warning system to connect with my body to make sure I'm living my best, healthiest life. It's an accountability partner, so instead of feeling angry or bitter, I feel thankful when I see the signs. I have a built-in alarm in tune with my body. Taking care of my health allows me to achieve remission and maintain it as long as possible.

Yoga is a practical tool to alchemize the past. Whether it's a childhood you can't forget or something so traumatic your mind erased the memories, trauma can leave you with a host of unpleasant symptoms, like always being on guard, irritability, anger outbursts, mood swings, self-destructive behavior, negative self-perception, anxiety, and depression, to name a few. But instead of being an obstacle to growth that mires us in pain, we own it, take control, and alchemize it. It's an example of the only way out is through.

I'm not a therapist, and this book isn't meant to deal with trauma psychologically; it's not even about trauma itself. This book is a testament to how I alchemized my trauma with yoga. It's a what, how, and why on the way yoga lets us alchemize our past. It brings the yoga practice—and what about your practice that leaves you feeling good—into your everyday life so you can transform your hardships, stress, and trauma into your best life.

Every time you're on your mat, you do something for yourself, even if it's only for five minutes. It's so hard to fit taking care of yourself into your daily life, but my goal is to make it easier. The yoga that I teach is a beginner-friendly, mainstream entry to something that goes beyond the superficial. You get fit, calm your mind, become physically resilient, and gain self-awareness. Yoga is a life practice. It's easy to start and maintain, even if it's the most basic poses for five minutes a day. And that's precisely the point I want to drive home: Five minutes a day is *better* for you than an hour once a week.

Why? Think of a flower about to blossom. If you set up a camera to record for enough hours, you can see it opening to a full bloom, little by little. The process is a combination of small moves that together add up to something powerful and magical. Look at every detail of each petal. All the little details and processes that must happen to create a single petal are part of the whole blooming transformation of the flower.

In other words, there are no shortcuts. You won't be able to skip or fast-forward your way through this. You won't blossom unless you've taken your time and your little steps every day to your destination, whatever that may be, metaphorically speaking. Yet if you commit to this, healing happens incidentally, as a result and a by-product of doing the work.

A *daily* yoga practice is what's going to change your life. An action that becomes ingrained in you, like brushing your teeth before bed. You wouldn't brush your teeth for one hour once a week and think that's going to equal good dental hygiene, right? Yoga is your mental, physical, spiritual, and emotional hygiene practice. For it to stick, there needs to be daily repetition and continuity. That's why we call it a practice. It's something you do repeatedly so you can be competent, progress, and reach your goals.

Even a short five minutes is beneficial. This helps you create a habit, forms muscle memory, and is an accumulation of strength and daily release. Think of a five-minute daily practice as 1 percent every day that adds up over time. A month becomes 30 percent, a year 365 percent. It's like compound interest earned on savings—one day, you wake up and realize you have a nice savings from simply putting in 1 percent every day.

Now here's the surprising part: When I say, "Even five minutes of yoga a day is better for you than once a week," I'm not only referring to a physical yoga practice. There is so much more to yoga than the poses and the flows. There are ways you can practice your yoga *off* the mat, too, like mindfulness, self-observation, nonattachment, and many more that I'll teach you in this book. It's when you take action and implement the little steps on a daily basis that the transformation will happen. So whether your five minutes are spent reading this book, doing the thought exercises, journaling, flowing through yoga poses, or just deep breathing, keep the steps of your trauma alchemy practice top of mind each day because the magic is in your daily practice. With trauma alchemy, you don't necessarily have to do any yoga at all, at least not in the physical sense. Simply read this book each day and do the work.

Why Read This (Whole) Book

If you've gone through hard times and you don't know how to get past them, there are guides and road maps to show you the way. Yoga is trauma alchemy; this book will teach you that.

My teaching style is modern, always explained in a clear and concise manner, without getting too woo-woo, so you can easily apply what I teach to everyday life. It's like *Extreme Ownership: How U.S. Navy Seals Lead and Win* but for yogis, where you move from victim of life to owner and shaper of your reality. Some victims don't want to be told they're not victims, but that won't help their growth, and that's not how I operate.

I'm a guide, not a guru, and trauma alchemy is *not* a never-ending hustle. It's also not a quick, easy fix. You were made to do hard things. You've already picked up this book; you're ready for this.

Trauma alchemy is not the same for everyone. Every journey and every trauma along the way is unique. No trauma is too big or too small. And please do not belittle or compare your experience with my own or anyone else's. The worst that has happened to you was the worst that has happened to you. And this work is all the same. I'm not just offering you a mindset or positive thinking; this is a practice with steps to follow. The yoga journey is a practice that ebbs and flows, just like trauma alchemy. You'll have sudden breakthroughs and bursts of energy, and other times, you'll have no interest and feel like you're falling behind. That's part of the practice as well.

You'll also find aspects of yourself that were already there. Personal and professional development are interconnected. They mirror each other. When one is off, it affects the other. I didn't believe I had the skills to make YouTube my career until I began my inner work and developing myself personally, peeling back the layers to reveal my true self. When you dive deeper, you shed what no longer serves you and discover parts of yourself that were there all along. At different times in your life, you'll uncover different experiences to work through. It could be that each time you reread this book, perhaps once every one or two years, it's a new experience—new self-discoveries, new releases, new trauma alchemies.

Yoga is being present, in the moment, whenever and wherever that moment may be. In that presence, we transcend the past and develop a solid foundation to deal with future hardships. Trauma alchemy is your off-the-mat yoga practice on steroids designed specifically to help you transform from a life of fight or flight to one of rest and relaxation. Imagine *savasana* clarity, but all the time. Through this practice, you become mindfully responsive instead of emotionally reactive. Through your daily practice, your whole nervous system changes, which changes your presence, your vibe. That changes how you respond to stressors, and it changes how you treat people and how people treat you. You won't be able to stop painful events from occurring. It's in nature that we find both order and chaos. But developing the strength and courage to withstand painful events and come out the other side is more than possible—it's necessary.

What happens in your life also happens on your mat. And vice versa—what you apply on the mat applies in your life off the mat. This book will show you how to see and embrace that connection.

And here's the best part: The different parts of a yoga session, from the grounding Child's Pose through the flows and the *savasana* at the end, align directly with the steps of trauma alchemy. We'll transform hardship, stress, and trauma into your best life using yoga as our guide. That's how this book is structured—like a yoga session, but for your life off the mat. This is not just a book you'll read, it's a book you'll *do*. And by working through this book, you will:

- Gain more clarity and eliminate confusion
- Feel more compassion for yourself and others
- Heal your nervous system
- Develop a more positive perspective about your day-to-day life
- Feel peaceful and connected instead of isolated
- Refine your yoga practice for healing and transformation
- Improve your relationship with your inner child
- Understand and let go of coping strategies that once served you but don't anymore
- Experience release

Trauma alchemy is a process of steps to complete, and yoga is the oasis in the desert of trauma. There are no shortcuts, and the alchemy part is personal to you. We meet at the intersection of understanding trauma alchemy and integrating your story. It's how *you* transmute and transform yourself through the power of yoga.

Your entire yoga practice has prepared you for this work. You are ready for it.

CHAPTER 2

GROUNDING

Everyone who gets on the yoga mat for the first time has had a breaking point in their life. Either something happened to you that pushed you to seek relief, or you're ready for serious rest and "me" time. That's when the grounding happens.

For me, the moment I felt broken in a way I never had been before was when I developed postpartum depression, for the third time, after an ectopic pregnancy. The nonviable fertilized egg had not implanted in my uterus. It was determined that it was somewhere in my abdomen and in the end was never found. This resulted in months of poking and prodding, chemo shots to prevent hemorrhage or death, and a *lot* of fear and anxiety. In retrospect, I'm thankful for that season of life, despite how difficult it was, because the depression became a catalyst for a major breakthrough in my life.

I began working with a new therapist—a psychiatrist, unlike the previous counselors I had seen. This wasn't the first time I had been pushed toward the brink and turned to therapy. I had been working with therapists for many years of my life, so I had been through this process before. At that point, I was thinking, *OK, let's just get this over with.*

The psychiatrist spent many weeks with me running through my childhood. This time was different. The sessions we spent poring over my past led to something new: a diagnosis. He diagnosed me with CPTSD. Unlike PTSD, which results from one major traumatic event, CPTSD is associated with repeated, lower-level trauma that continues over an extended period, building into something problematic.

What kind of lower-level trauma? Being diagnosed with ulcerative colitis, I've lived with a chronic and incurable disease since I was a little girl. At times, this bowel disease that causes ulcers and inflammation in the large colon is debilitating physically and emotionally. Not only that, but I was also raised in a dysfunctional family setting and parentified by my own parents who, although they did their best at the time, were emotionally incapable of meeting my needs. This led to what was essentially a family divorce and finding familiarity in an emotionally avoidant and abusive romantic relationship in my teens. All this carried lasting trauma into my adulthood.

Seeing the psychiatrist nearly thirty years later would completely shift my life and open my eyes to what had happened to me and why I felt the way I felt in the present as a mom of two and dealing with all the medical interventions and fear surrounding the ectopic pregnancy. Finally having a concrete diagnosis of CPTSD gave me a newfound clarity and even a sense of hope. I mark that as the beginning of my healing journey.

That was when I began grounding.

In yoga, grounding is the first stage after you step on your mat. It's about rooting yourself to the earth, feeling strong and solid in your mind and body. Grounding is both physical and spiritual. We practice this physically by performing specific yoga poses in a proper stance and alignment. If you're standing, then you ground down through each part of your feet to create a solid connection with the earth. If you're grounding in Child's Pose, then you feel your knees, shins, forehead, and arms rest on your mat as your hips relax. If you're seated, then you ground through your hips, thighs, and ankles. Really, whatever part of you makes contact with the ground, you create a solid connection with the ground that supports you.

Besides doing the actual poses, we ground spiritually through meditation, sensory deprivation, and breathing exercises. When you ground down, you tune out the world and take a pause from everything else happening in your life. You tune out so you can tune in to yourself. When you ground yourself, you become present. Self-awareness and focusing on your breath and state of being in that moment help you do this, and this in turn connects us to our true self and helps to shift away from outer elements beyond our control. This is the spiritual aspect of grounding, and it works in tandem with the physical poses to connect us energetically to the earth below us.

In trauma alchemy, you take what you do on the mat and apply it in your everyday life. You use the principles and practices of yoga to alchemize your trauma. Grounding in your life means taking a break from your reality to turn inward, to look at a very specific moment in time or set of experiences to begin the healing journey. People avoid this because they feel reactive when doing it. This is different from what you may have tried before when you felt unsafe to go there. Grounding, for you, is establishing that safe space. You can detach from the negative emotions that have made this inner work so challenging, even impossible, because it has been too hard.

In this chapter, in this stage of your trauma alchemy practice, you will self-reflect, but in a deeper and more action-oriented way than you may have before in therapy alone, with mindfulness, or through some other personal development practice. Self-reflection in trauma alchemy means looking at yourself in the third person while detaching from your feelings. You'll become aware of what is happening and what has happened without emotional attachment.

But why is it important to emotionally detach?

It's not that attachment is bad or wrong. We become emotionally attached to our partner, our children, and our friends so we can bond and form relationships; it's an essential part of being alive. The issue is when we remain connected to past events, negative emotions that cause us stress, and situations and people that don't serve us. We end up feeling anxious, depressed, and resentful when these emotions become trapped in our body. If you're upset and too in your feelings, it's harder to calmly reflect on yourself. Emotional detachment helps us to observe ourselves and our life with greater clarity and accuracy, and can then help us see where we need to change and improve. (Later in the chapter, I will give you an exercise using this very technique.) This is why yoga is effective in facilitating emotional detachment—the poses and breath work help us focus on the present while releasing stress and negative feelings, and as a result, we're able to control our emotions and move forward in a calm state.

What happened in my past—and what happened in yours, too—left us with feelings of anxiety, anger, depression . . . pick the negative emotion. Our anger and anxiety served a purpose at the time, though. Anxiety develops to keep us alert in an unsafe environment. Anger reminds us to be vigilant about how others treat us. In other words, while considered negative and even destructive emotions, they initially served to protect us. It's the mind and body's inner response to the unpredictability or the instability of the outer world. But now that time has passed and you're no longer in the same situations, these emotions hurt and hinder your progress. Anger, anxiety, depression, and resentment can evolve into guilt and shame, and over time can become your new identity. When that happens, you can feel stuck in these feelings, like a victim to your own reality.

It doesn't have to be this way, though. There *is* a way out. We're going to shift your mindset from victim to owner, beginning now.

Let's get grounded.

But First . . . Breathe

To help you do this, let's belly breathe together—in and out, through your nose. Place your hand on your belly just above your belly button. Breathe slowly and deeply, feeling your belly expanding and then contracting under your hand. Just feel your belly slowly expand and contract, inflate and deflate; that's the first step.

People who are stuck in fight-or-flight trauma responses have short, shallow chest breaths all the time, which leads to shortness of breath and often anxiety throughout the day. If this is you, practice your belly breathing daily. Use it anytime you're feeling stressed, anxious, tense, or you simply notice that your breathing has shifted to short, shallow chest breaths. All it takes is three to five deep belly breaths to shift your state from hurried and overwhelmed to calm and grounded.

In fact, at any point while reading this book if you feel ungrounded, upset, insecure, or uncomfortable, take a moment to pause and do this breathing exercise. And after you've read the book, you can keep doing the exercise daily to calm your nervous system and take back control.

Detachment Means Freedom . . . from Emotions

Close your eyes and imagine a movie theater. You're alone in the front row, looking up at the big screen. It's dark and quiet. But instead of seeing your favorite actor, you see yourself acting on-screen. And you're seeing moments of your life play out before you. As you're watching the scene unfold, instead of feeling the emotions the performer feels, you're feeling what the audience feels watching a scene like this. Whether that actor is you at age six, twelve, or twenty-seven, you're not those people anymore. They are past versions of you that you are now examining in the third person.

Watching my childhood on-screen for the first time allowed me to release decades of anger and resentment, and to feel instead a deep sadness for this child. I was seeing myself as a child but from the vantage point of an adult, rewatching my own painful experiences. What I felt for the first time was grief, not rage. I was grieving for the loss of so much of my childhood, something I had never done before. Seeing myself as a child was like seeing a hurting and angry lion cub in a cage. Along with grief, I felt tremendous compassion. Developing compassion for myself as a child allowed me to acknowledge her pain, grieve for her, and finally let go of her anger, with calm and forgiveness.

Watching my biography in the imaginary theater also made me see others' role in my story with compassion. I was able to see the pain everyone else felt amid that. When I was a child, I felt resentment. But in that moment, watching my past unfold on-screen, I saw the other characters and what they had to endure, like my mom. I saw her doing the absolute best she knew how to do at the time, which is a far cry from how I saw her during those difficult times. Instead of seeing her as an emotionally unstable mother who didn't love me the way I needed, I saw her as a person—a young woman and single mother—with flaws, strengths, and pain of her own. I saw her as a *whole* person *in context*.

If you stop hyperfocusing on one aspect of a memory, you start to notice everything else happening in your life at that time. For me, by looking right at it, I was able to shift my focus from my childhood illness and all the fighting. Now I'm able to see the good times, like crafting with my mom, playing piano at my dad's, enjoying holidays, or simply playing outside with my brother and grandma. It's almost like you lose those years of your life when you forget *what else* happened.

That began the path of forgiveness, and it's essential because of what you're going to be able to do next.

Detachment Means Freedom . . . from Identity

I identified with my emotions. I was who and how I felt. For thirty-two years, I was that angry six-year-old. I saw myself as somebody who was wounded, somebody who needed to fight to defend herself. And so that pattern continued throughout my life. As long as I held on to those emotions, I was stuck in a repeating pattern, like an emotional loop. Yet when I was able to turn the tables and watch myself in my own story, that was the beginning of me breaking that pattern. I saw that I no longer needed the armor I had built around me and that I didn't have to be constantly on the defense. Everyone who has experienced trauma has had to endure that. Patterns present themselves until you deal with and learn from them. Emotional attachment is part of identity. To release the emotional attachment, you must also release the identification you have created with that. (You may notice that the phrases "my trauma," "my anxiety," or "my disease" never appear in this book.)

I used to attach myself to the guilt and shame of bleeding during bowel movements every day, remaining chronically underweight, having food anxiety, being bedridden. The diarrhea was a bright, blood red, and there were days where I would have to use the toilet more than a dozen times. As a child, I didn't understand how truly sick I was. Out of fear and embarrassment, I said nothing and did nothing about it, and instead I became my own caretaker during those years. When I watched that movie in the movie theater exercise, I saw this child as she was—a kid who needed medical attention, caring for and defending herself.

Grounding yourself in a new, stable, calm vantage point as you look at your life puts a helpful, healthy barrier between you and how you've felt, who you've been, who you've seen yourself as. In yoga, these are the long, calm breaths, often done in Child's Pose or seated on your mat—grounded.

New Grounding in Stability and Security

In this chapter, we are detaching who you are from what happened to you in the past. You'll soon be able to leave past trauma behind where it belongs and move forward into your brighter future.

First, think about any lingering pain you might be holding on to as a full backpack you carry wherever you go. Imagine the weight on your shoulders, the inconvenience of dragging this load around. Now imagine taking the backpack off your shoulders and leaving it behind. How much lighter would you feel? If you had nothing weighing you down, how different would your life be?

The key to achieving this is to trust the process of trauma alchemy. This isn't fake it till you make it. You must do the steps and the work to get the results. But if you do, you will come out on the other side lighter than before. Your identity doesn't need to be wrapped up in your past or whom you used to be; you can let it go. It's history, anyway.

The main way that you detach from your past is to see it as a matter of fact. Instead of focusing on how you feel or how your body reacts, you step back and observe it from a neutral position. Put your emotions to the side, resist the urge to label or analyze the event, and instead look at the situation as "This is what happened." That's it. Something happened to you in the past, and it came from outside you, not within you. When you attach a past trauma to your identity, it becomes an anchor that keeps you stuck in the same place mentally and physically. But when you put distance between yourself and the event, you can see it as separate from yourself, and then you can release it.

This is where yoga comes in. You learn to self-reflect without emotional attachment or blaming yourself or others. As a result, your identity is freed up from your past, becoming as present as you are.

Detachment Means Freedom . . . from Victimhood

The movie exercise allows you to see the situation from a bird's-eye view (or moviegoer's perspective). Seeing my life from this perspective helped me shift from blame to compassion.

Whereas I used to think, *I was the child. You were the adult. This never should have happened,* I've now shifted to, *She did the best she knew how at the time. Yes, there is a child here who was hurting. There is also a mother who was hurting, too.*

That one shift took me out of victimhood, not only in the present, but also in the past and future. It doesn't mean I took ownership of what happened to me—I was a child, and I wasn't responsible for things that I had no control over. It means that instead of being triggered and reacting, I'm choosing to respond. And you and I can do that now. We have ownership over our present and future choices. Being in a position to choose a response over a reaction is where we get our power to overcome the negative emotions that hold us back.

You can rewrite your reality because your life is a story, and it's *your* story to create. In fact, let's do that right now. Take your movie theater experience and write it *all* down. This is exactly what I did after I went to my movie. It took me a couple of hours, and it was emotional and heavy. But it's normal to feel intense emotions when you do this. This is where they come into play.

Journal it out with a pen and paper or in your notes on your phone. Start from the beginning, and give yourself time and space to document the exercise. As the third-party observer watching actors in the story of your life, what do you see happening? Write in third person (use "she" or "he" to refer to who you were/are), but don't make the characters protagonists and antagonists in a battle of good and evil. Instead, write what happened as if you're writing a report. It's the process of writing the visual exercise that lets you experience the emotions that come with observing it. Let your emotions come out; don't shove them down or reject them. Let them flow through you so you can be free from them.

When you've written everything you can, you can do what you like with your journal; this never needs to be read again. You can light it with a match or toss it in the nearest fire pit. You can shred it or throw it in the trash. The grounding of all these feelings into a single account of what happened—and even destroying or deleting the document afterward—is cathartic. You'll feel lighter, more stable, safe, present, and grounded.

If you feel that this exercise becomes too intense at any point, please go back to the breathing exercise from earlier in this chapter to help ground yourself. Or if you feel you're not ready for any reason, or you feel you may cause yourself injury or to self-harm, or you just want a supportive guide by your side, then please pause and seek professional help from a licensed therapist or qualified counselor before reattempting it. There is no shame in getting the help you need. I've received many, many years of guidance from professional therapists, and I now consider it my secret weapon against what drags me down. It's helpful and supportive as a mother and a business owner. Therapy does not mean brokenness.

Grounded and Free

Through therapy, the movie theater exercise, and my journal of the experience, I gained a perspective about my childhood that I never had before. Having ulcerative colitis and being gravely ill from ages five to twelve was not only physically painful and debilitating. The experience left deep unseen scars in my psyche. To see that situation without emotional attachment and in a calm state was the true grounding for me.

After years of no contact due to conflict and instability, my mom and I built a new relationship. I appreciate her determination now; my mom is *so* strong. I'm proud of her for who she is and who she has become.

I'm proud of the hard work she has done over her lifetime and especially since we've rekindled a relationship. Now, with the passage of time and progress on my own journey, I can admire my mom for her own story. She dealt with intergenerational and systemic trauma. As an immigrant, she faced barriers I can't even imagine. Her role in my story is but one side of the *full* story—my mother's story. I'm honored we have returned to each other's lives. I cannot imagine my life without her.

My mom is creative, brave, and wonderful with my kids. She has leaned into *nanima*—the Hindi word for "maternal grandmother" and "wisewoman"—and she lives that role for me and her grandchildren. She is whole and complete now and enjoyable to be around. I realize how much I love her and how much I craved her love as a child. The difference now is that when issues arise, we can discuss them while preserving our relationship. I was able to see her for who she was *then*, which helped me see her for who she is *now*. That would not have been possible had I not done this work and the exercise of journaling out my movie theater experience.

Some parents are better in their relationship with their children when they're kids, while others form a healthy bond when their children are grown. My mother and I experienced the latter. Our relationship started out rough, but we were able to mend the broken parts and completely transform our mother-daughter bond. We still have some boundaries, but over the years, those boundaries have softened quite a bit.

What we've covered in this chapter is the first step in the process of trauma alchemy. Grounding anchors us to the earth and keeps us steady and secure. It's only when we ground ourselves fully that we establish a solid base to move further toward transforming ourselves. This prepares us for each step forward in this sequence.

Now, with your body grounded, your breath calm, and your focus present, it's time to get moving.

CHAPTER 3

WARM UP

Nearly two decades ago, as a teenager, before I met Leland, I was stuck in an abusive and dysfunctional romantic relationship. I dated this teenage boy for the entirety of my high school years, during which we broke up and reunited more than a dozen times.

Soon after our fourth anniversary, something in me snapped, or at least woke me up. It dawned on me that I was entrenched in a seriously bad relationship. It had been my decision to stay after everything that had happened, and it was I who had put myself there. My *mindset* was keeping me trapped in abusive patterns. I was letting myself be destroyed for nothing. The only way out of that situation was to find a way through.

I was guided with a single realization: I wanted to be a mother someday. But I didn't want to be a human shield for my future children. This newfound self-awareness struck me like a lightning bolt. I had a rush of confidence and self-belief. It was like I had been driving around in circles and finally found an exit.

I knew that change, though necessary, would be uncomfortable. But it would be worth it.

Just seeing patterns makes them easier to break, but it takes more than awareness to move out of your comfort zone, though. It takes willingness. In yoga, thinking, *I'm doing this,* is a conscious choice you make right before the warm-up. It's going to be uncomfortable if you haven't moved around a lot that day and are unfamiliar with a new flow. You may look silly doing it, even if you've been a yogi for years. All these are necessary steps toward growth, change, and self-transformation—in yoga and in life.

Getting Comfortable with Discomfort

In the SarahBethYoga community, all my yoga videos include warm-ups. We start with grounding, and then we warm up by moving our body. This movement and the stretching involved might feel difficult for the first couple of minutes. That's normal. It's to be expected. It's in the discomfort that we grow.

During the warm-up, we center the movements around the spine and focus on getting those vertebrae moving. Did you know the spine can move in six directions? Most people don't move their bodies in more than one way on a typical day. So the first time they do, they feel it . . . strongly.

For many people, this new, unfamiliar movement feels good—at first. That's because most of us learn bad posture from years of desk work and office chairs, which these warm-up stretches correct. People who adopt a victim mentality will also often find themselves hunched over, head down, and go around like that all day. The warm-up forces them to raise their chins and their gaze, physically and emotionally.

Warm-up stretching starts to feel uncomfortable when your body begins giving feedback. *There's tension here . . . Tightness over there . . . This area doesn't move like it used to . . . Oof.* Years of unhelpful posture patterns have taken a toll. Fortunately, this knowledge alone can motivate self-care choices like buying an ergonomic desk chair or adjusting the back of your car seat.

And putting your body in these new positions counteracts old patterns and emotional states. Shifting to new thought patterns may lead to similar discomfort. You're becoming aware of what you couldn't—or didn't want to—see before. Allowing yourself to see the patterns showing up in your body and life reveals what needs work next.

Change Your Patterns, Change Your Life

At one point in time, I was taking ibuprofen three times a week for stress-related headaches. And I experienced four to six debilitating migraines a year; some even sent me to the hospital. Counting the migraine hangover, I would lose three days of my life each time.

And the danger of losing my awareness to a migraine haunted me. I had a couple of migraines while I was alone with my infant son. I remember lying on the floor beside him with an ice pack on my head, repeating to myself, *Something's gotta change, something's gotta change,* almost like a mantra.

The doctors I spoke to all said my regular headaches and migraines were stress-related. They also told me something I found surprising at the time: My serotonin was most likely low.

I brought this up to my therapist, who replied, "I'm not surprised at all that you're low in serotonin. I agree."

Why was my serotonin low? Because I was living in fight-or-flight mode.

To deal with this issue, I went on a preventative headache medication—and it worked! But after a year, I learned that this medicine was correlated with early-onset dementia. That was a deal-breaker, so with my doctor's guidance, I got off the medicine. And it meant I needed to fix my serotonin levels.

I reexamined patterns like overworking and overusing screens. And I created new patterns like using blue-light blockers, setting personal screen-time limits, delegating tasks to others, and placing significant boundaries around my work schedule. And whenever I felt a headache coming on, I would stop what I was doing, sometimes for the day, and lay down with an eye mask for a twenty-minute *savasana*, then contemplate what may have triggered that headache and how I could prevent it next time.

So yes, I'm not as hyperproductive as I used to be, and I'm not meeting the insane work expectations I once had for myself, but I'm much more relaxed and I'm still getting work done, just at a more leisurely and sustainable pace.

Not only haven't I had a migraine in two years, but the headaches are now rare occurrences—all without medication! That's the power of noticing and breaking patterns. It works so well, you can change your brain chemistry and heal yourself.

Patterns aren't just physical, but mental and emotional, too. They all connect to one another. Your emotional state can result in poor posture, for example. And every part of your mind and body connects to the larger ecosystem of your being.

You might notice how certain problems seem to arise again and again, despite your best efforts: "How come every time I date a guy, book a trip, or see my parents, this same thing happens?" These are all patterns, and they manifest in our daily thoughts and actions, often unconsciously. That's why they're called patterns. Your mind resembles a computer, and once you have a certain program running, it continues even if you're not conscious of it. As we've seen, lack of awareness enables a pattern to keep running.

In trauma alchemy, awareness and change support each other. Becoming conscious of patterns allows you to break them. It can be uncomfortable in the beginning, but trust in the change and growth awaiting you on the other side.

How Patterns Reveal Themselves to You

Patterns will continue to present themselves in your life until you learn from them. They are lessons, and you discover them by entering a general state of self-awareness. So become aware of yourself: your body, your thoughts, and your emotions. Tune out the outside world so you can tune in to yourself.

It's important to reduce stimulation. Get away from screens, turn off background music or shows, and close your eyes. Focus on self-talk and self-observation. (Did you know that self-observation is an off-the-mat yoga practice?) Now sit there and take it all in. What patterns have you experienced in your life? Continue the journal you began in the previous chapter, and brain-dump it all on the page. That means writing *everything*: the good, the bad, the ugly, and the beautiful.

Write about whatever you're proud of or frustrated with right now. Are they similar in some way? And the patterns that you're recognizing, what can you learn from them? How did they once serve you? How are they no longer serving you?

That simple awareness of tuning out to tune in will let you notice and capture these patterns as they appear. Journaling regularly supports this process. When you do it, notice when you write the same thought, hope, or struggle again and again to help you spot a pattern.

It's different for everyone. Even after I saw the pattern with my ex-boyfriend, it took a while for me to embrace the discomfort of change. But in time, I realized that being uncomfortable alone was better than being comfortable and abused.

Shifting from Victim to Freedom

Most people who've experienced some type of trauma have felt victimized. We talked about this in Chapter 2, and it bears further discussion. People who seem stuck in a victimhood mindset exhibit certain patterns, even if they're desperate to change. They may . . .

- Take offense easily
- Feel under attack
- Think people are out to get them
- Find it hard to trust others
- Have difficulty creating and maintaining deep, meaningful relationships

- Struggle to maintain jobs, reputations, etcetera
- Have a hard time seeing good in the world, much less abundance
- See injustice and unfairness everywhere

Do you see any of these tendencies in yourself?

Victimhood patterns aren't black and white. They become part of your identity after they have developed into a program. And that's when they block you from opportunities like positive relationships, needed support, a stable job, and more.

I'm not referring to the law of attraction, nor am I telling you, "Just think positively!" However, you cannot drive forward while staring in the rearview mirror. A beautiful future doesn't come from focusing on a dark past.

Know this: It's not your fault, but you *are* responsible for what happens next. You did the best you knew how at the time. Look at yourself with compassion, regardless of who's at fault.

Here's the key: Release guilt and shame first because these feelings will hold you back. They are internal burdens more burdensome than carrying a backpack full of rocks day in and day out.

When you're ready to let go of guilt and shame, you can move toward feeling empowered. And self-empowerment often results in increased motivation, which can lead to a new state of being. Your everyday baseline changes.

Some doubt that it's possible. But it is, and I'll get you there. If you have noticed victimhood patterns in your feelings and thoughts, go back to your journal. *What* choices did you make before you felt those feelings and thought those thoughts? *Why* did you make those choices?

Let me give you an example from my life. After I had my first child, I suffered from postpartum depression. So I had a drink or two every night to cope. But I didn't like daily drinking; it wasn't me. I talked to my therapist, who asked me why I was doing it if I didn't like it.

I said, "I need an exhale. I'm alone all day, and my husband works seven days a week, sixteen hours a day. I'm cooped up in a tiny apartment." The drinking wasn't the real point, but it was the ritual I had created just to have a moment to myself.

Becoming aware of this habit and why I had picked it up made me realize I needed multiple "exhale" moments throughout the day. That way, I wouldn't get to the point of feeling like I had to drink alcohol just to relax.

I went to mommy and baby group therapy classes and started taking my baby to childcare at the gym so I could exercise or just take a shower. I also began the process of scheduled feeding, playing, and sleeping instead of the on-demand nursing that had once served us. All of this worked. And I replaced the alcoholic drink with a soothing, tasty, magnesium beverage or a Zevia (a sugar-free, stevia-sweetened soda)—much healthier alternatives than alcohol.

These changes didn't seem significant on the surface, but they added up to a healthier, happier, and calmer me. Recognizing the harm of drinking nightly and realizing why I was doing it helped me see that new pattern and break it. So talking to a qualified professional such as a therapist can be crucial because others can glean insights about your thoughts and feelings that you don't see. The professional and objective input that a therapist can provide can help you fast-track your growth and ease the pain of what's ailing you.

Quitting cold turkey doesn't work. I drank to fill a void in my life. The answer was filling it with healthy alternatives that helped my condition instead of making it worse.

Ask yourself how you can take responsibility for making different choices—to keep yourself from thinking, feeling, or acting in that way again. That's how you break the pattern.

Just as important, what are you going to replace the pattern with? If you're experiencing victimhood patterns, replace wallowing with a broader perspective. Ask yourself, "What if?," before the pattern activates: "What if that's this person's best effort?" "What if this tragedy has great meaning?"

The more painful those victimhood triggers, the harder this may be. It's not about being grateful for being abused, a debilitating bowel disease, or an ectopic pregnancy. It's about reinterpreting them, giving yourself a sliver of permission to experience a sense of gratitude.

Some bad experiences aren't our fault. As children, for instance, we had little control of our environments. But now, as an adult, you can reclaim your power. You have the agency to move forward—and to choose *how* you move forward.

Some people who desire to break free from victimhood patterns need to replace the influences in their lives. It's hard to take ownership when your friends or media influencers are promoting victimhood. Set boundaries and take time away from them if necessary. Be sure to take these steps with mindfulness and grace. Everybody is on their own path. This is not about judging others for where they are in their journey but instead recognizing when there are relationships that are holding you back and gently create space from them so you can continue to grow. Just know that your growth can serve as a mirror to those who are still stuck in their patterns. Their reaction to your growth is less of a reflection on you and more of a reflection on where they are in their own journey. Keep moving, even if you're moving alone. You are all that you need.

Tuning out to tune in includes setting healthy boundaries. Find new people who are living how you want to live. If they're not to be found in your day-to-day life, follow them on social media, watch their videos, and listen to their podcasts. Seek out anyone you can relate to who has a growth mindset instead of a fixed mindset. A fixed mindset thinks, *It is what it is, and it's not going to change.* That's peak victimhood.

A growth mindset understands that it's possible to grow and overcome the mental blocks you struggle with, even if it seems impossible right now. Just one shift in your beliefs can unlock ownership and stop victimhood patterns.

Never confuse slow progress with no progress. Someone following a new health regimen to lose forty pounds may feel defeated after losing four pounds in a month. But extending that small success over ten months will add up to the desired goal. Incremental changes over time create big transformations in the future.

Let's go back and look at yoga in light of what we've learned. The warm-up will have your shoulders, spine, and posture looking as if a burden has been lifted from you. It lets you be open, aware, and confident from taking ownership.

That's what yoga and trauma alchemy are all about. If you get through the warm-up, chances are you'll want to keep going. *It feels good.* And it feels even better to be in control of your destiny.

Remember, your daily practice includes reading this book, doing the work, and integrating both with your yoga. You're *moving* into new territory, internally and externally.

Let's continue . . .

CHAPTER 4

INTENTION

When Leland and I first started dating when I was eighteen, I confided in him that I had a hard time visualizing my life past the age of twenty-five. You would think a young college student like I was then would think she had her whole life ahead of her. Yet I couldn't see myself living past twenty-five, and I didn't know why. I thought it was an omen, a sign.

So Leland jarred me when he asked, "Don't you think that's a self-fulfilling prophecy?"

I had never heard that phrase before. "What does that mean?"

"It means you're making it happen by saying it and believing it."

I had never heard before that your thoughts and beliefs can directly affect reality. The only time I had even considered something approaching that concept was on the yoga mat.

Back then, I went to a chain yoga studio whenever I found time, which wasn't often. At the beginning of each practice, right after I would get grounded to start, the yoga teacher would say something about setting an intention. I had honestly thought she had meant a mantra like, "Breathe" or "Gratitude." Not something I wanted to make happen by intending it. But that conversation led me to rediscover the transformative power of setting an intention in yoga—and in life.

In yoga, intention begins at the end of the warm-up. You typically place your hands together at heart center, settle down, find your breath, close your eyes, and set your intention.

Your yoga class may include a themed talk, but typical intentions are "Presence," "Let go," and "Be here now." However, these are a bit cliché. In SarahBethYoga, we set intentions based on the accompanying talk. Sometimes the intention chooses you (like with intention cards). Sometimes the intention is not chosen consciously. Instead, it reveals itself through what has happened—or what is going to happen—that day.

How to Know What You Want

Intention means you know what you want. On the surface, it sounds simple. But the trouble is, most people don't know what they want. And often it's because we've talked ourselves out of whatever that is because of other people's expectations of us. It's important to have your result in mind and not listen to others to the point that you forget who you are.

Intention is not about what you *think* you want. It's what you *truly* want. To know the difference, you need to get to the root of yourself. Are your basic needs being met? Everyone has different priorities, but beyond the physiological and safety bottom levels of psychologist Abraham Maslow's hierarchy of needs, what three desires do you prioritize most? These are the decision-makers for everything you do.

In my case, I want and need security, family, and growth. Leland wants and needs family and growth as well, but he values spontaneity more than security.

When I talk about your true wants, I don't mean external, imposed desires. Is what you want chosen or imposed? External, imposed priorities often hide behind thoughts like . . .

I'm supposed to . . .

I have to . . .

I should . . .

They come from outside of us rather than from inside our core selves.

But what's the difference between imposed and chosen priorities, and where does this issue come from?

When we're kids, we seem to know what we want. But over time, the influence of others can cloud our sense of self and our deepest desires, and we talk ourselves out of what we want based on other people's expectations.

Think of all the times you've heard people say, "You should want this. You have to do that." On a subconscious level, society's expectations and opinionated family and friends can talk us out of our true wants. When we are too influenced by others, a part of us becomes stifled. Our individual desires get buried in a barrage of "shoulds."

It's our parents' job to raise us with their own expectations. They're part of what made us who we are, and for that, we can be grateful. But to grow, we must transcend those expectations. Becoming our own adult means we must free ourselves from the nest and fly, finding our true selves and desires along the way.

You're an adult now, and you're reading this book. So it's time for you to take responsibility and leave the nest. Tune out the shoulds, have to's, and expectations, and really ask yourself, "What do *I* want?"

Consider your priorities. They help you find your direction but not always the right result. But understanding your priorities is the first step toward setting intentions. Your three highest wants and needs set your due north. And your priorities become a checklist for everything that falls within those parameters.

How do you know what your true highest priorities are?

For starters, look at your bank account. You can identify what you want and value based on what you're spending your money on. Are you buying based on your own priorities or what has been imposed on you?

Let's do a thought experiment. Imagine all your possessions, whether they be material goods or services you pay for. Now imagine losing them all and being left with nothing. Of all the things you owned and lost, what do you want back the most? What possessions come to mind first and make you feel the most loss?

Your highest priorities reveal themselves as you think about them, and this exercise is a way to put them to the test. This helps you come to understand them beyond the shallow or practical. When you see deeper than the object itself, you begin to see the meaning behind the material item and what's drawing you to it.

For example, if you thought of your bed, maybe that's the place where you recover from physical and mental exhaustion. If you invested in a high-quality mattress, it may mean you rely on a good night's sleep to function. And if not having the right bed has a major negative effect on your life, then your priority isn't the bed itself. It's your overall well-being.

That's why we do this exercise—to examine the true meaning of our desires through our material possessions.

Let me ask you another question: Where do your thoughts tend to go when you're daydreaming?

Similar to imagining losing all your possessions, this exercise has a narrowing effect. Maybe you often think about an upcoming cruise. Is it because you value cruises as one of your highest priorities? Maybe it's because you like knowing what to expect and don't like surprises. You want to ensure everything goes according to plan. If that's the case, perhaps your real priority is security. That's why it's vital to look below the surface for meaning.

Being able to go beyond others' expectations of you is challenging. Finding the self-awareness and courage to see your true self takes confidence and ownership. But to own your highest priorities is priceless.

Often these experiments can trigger negative feelings. You may feel guilt or shame for wanting something different from what you have—something better. It's easy to say, "Be yourself," or "Be authentic." But it's the most difficult journey an individual can take.

Human beings learn to live by observing and imitating others. That's fine because we are social creatures. The village provides us with safety, security, and a sense of belonging. But it also represses us, keeping us in a "comfortable" state and blurring the line between the individual and the group.

By getting tangled up in what others think we should do, we can lose ourselves and our true desires. To break from the group, find authentic personal values, and embrace your true identity is a courageous act. It means risking exile and being alone. It may be a brutal fact, but it's unavoidable, and it's necessary for self-discovery. In the end, your self-love gives others permission to do the same.

Many of our priorities come down to self-worth. People suffering from low self-worth may feel unworthy of what they desire. They can feel guilt and shame for even wanting it.

Some tie their self-worth to unhealthy or unattainable priorities, like productivity. For example, I thought I had to always be producing something in order to have worth. And not only that, what I produced had to be good. I was tying my self-worth to others' feedback on my yoga videos.

Then I realized, I'm not a human doing . . . I'm a human being . And *being* is truly a *miracle*. The fact that I can experience this world—to taste, communicate, love—is the most amazing feeling ever. Loving and connecting is my purpose. This revelation allowed me to detach my self-worth from what I produce and how people respond to it.

What have you been tying your self-worth to? How can you shift it to simply *being*?

This shift in your self-worth will take you from where you are to where you want to be.

And where's that?

By this point in the practice, you know some of the wants and needs behind your intention. So you see your destination more clearly. And your decisions and actions are swayed by your newfound clarity and self-awareness.

When I realized that the abusive ex-boyfriend wasn't the future I intended, one including a happy family and healthy, safe children, I broke a cycle that was years of on-again, off-again abuse. I had a bigger purpose. I knew I deserved better, and I didn't stop until I got better. Two weeks after that final breakup, I met Leland.

When you see the future that you intend for yourself, you also see who and what is not in that future. Change your perspective, and everything else changes. It's as if the world changes as you transform yourself.

Your Intention

Let's help you get clarity about your priorities, then identify your wants and needs so you can fulfill those priorities.

Return to your journal. It's as simple as writing, *I'm going to move forward with* _____ *in my life,* or brain-dumping all your intentions. Eventually, when you're ready, distill your intention down to one or two words. Choose words that are powerful but easy to remember.

It's OK if nothing meaningful emerges as you journal. Perhaps you'll even freeze up. If that's the case, then let's set an intention for yourself as you read the rest of this book: *Growth.*

This simple, one-word intention gives you permission to try new things to alchemize, to transform, to take up space, to own your space. To help you grow. We'll explore the importance of growth more in the next chapter.

Going forward, you'll be able to judge every situation according to your intention. You'll know what to do that you're not doing. Intention becomes a self-fulfilling prophecy *you* are in control of. Once you know your intention, opportunities to follow through on it will present themselves.

You've already broken patterns, so this is how you move forward. Because your next step—in yoga and in life—is to move. A lot. Keep your result, your intention, in mind to guide you along the way, and stay focused because there will be ebb-and-flow moments. There will be yo-yoing. Some moments will be intense, others relaxed. Sometimes you will have setbacks, but they will teach you wisdom if you let your intention guide you.

CHAPTER 5

SUN A—BAM FLOW

I almost quit SarahBethYoga in 2017. At that time in my life, I was overwhelmed with my business. In retrospect, it makes perfect sense. After all, I was the classic solo entrepreneur. I did everything myself: marketing, emails, filming, editing, and anything else that needed to be done. To say my position was stressful and high demand is an understatement.

In addition to the workload I was carrying alone, I was also deep in postpartum depression while taking care of my infant son. And I reached my breaking point. Something had to change. So when Leland secured a new job, one with a stable income, I was afforded the opportunity to take a rest, and I took it.

You see, right before this, Leland had filed bankruptcy on the bar he had owned and operated for several years and, within a couple of weeks, had gotten this job. It was a night-and-day difference in our lives, and I felt like I could finally rest. I was at my breaking point.

I'm just taking a break, I told my audience. But the truth is I didn't know if I was coming back. I shut down my computer for what ended up being three months straight. During that time, I slowed down and planned each day. Every day, I took my son out for a walk and connected with him through developmental play. I cooked for my family and took care of my hygiene and sleep.

Those actions not only improved my overall well-being, but they helped alleviate my postpartum depression and allowed me to be in tune with my son. I went from a breaking point to a turning point in three months.

That turning point arrived at my son's first birthday party. I spent hours every single day custom-designing a monster-themed birthday party, complete with handmade decorations, monster cupcakes, and a handmade monster box that could hold cards with its teeth.

But the day of the party, it snowed twelve inches. Only one person showed up. I experienced all kinds of stress ahead of the party. When I looked around at everything I had put together and at the one parent who had shown up, I thought to myself, *I need a better outlet for my creativity. My child is only one year old. He doesn't care about any of this!*

At that moment, I realized that it was time to return to SarahBethYoga—this time more mindfully. So I hired a videographer and an editor. I also hired someone to help with childcare and learned how to delegate even more.

Also, I decided to relaunch SarahBethYoga with an app. I had dreamed of offering online memberships, and it seemed the perfect time to make that dream a reality. Leland got a new job at a company that developed white-label apps. So within a couple of months, we launched our app. Overnight, we went from making $4,000 a month to $40,000 per month. Then, just a few months later, I asked Leland to quit his job to join me and build SarahBethYoga together.

I took a risk when I quit for those three months. And when I threw myself into party planning, I told myself it was for my son—a baby who had no idea what was going on. As Leland and I always remind each other, "Take the leap, then fly." No matter what happens, you learn. And even if you fall, you've got nowhere to go but up. Everything I did during my break was part of my growth. It helped me see that vanity metrics—social media likes, follows, comments—didn't matter anymore. They were a nice part of building a brand. But like the monster box I had designed, they weren't the point. And this was the shift to working smarter, not harder.

Even going overboard with the birthday party showed me what I needed next for growth: an appropriate creative outlet. That was my sign to return to SarahBethYoga as a source of creativity and income. So even though that party had no impact on anyone, what came out of it has had an impact on the world.

Restarting SarahBethYoga took endurance and perseverance, not hustle or grindset. This relaunch and what took me from breaking point to turning point was about ruthless persistence in a routine. And that routine involved intention, delegation, work/life boundaries, and the simplest but most effective morning and evening self-care routines. (More about that in a moment.)

In yoga, the first flow of a session—called Sun Salutation A, or Sun A—is a routine made up of a simple sequence of poses that are repeated for several minutes to increase blood flow, improve mobility, and prepare your body for more intense poses and flows to come.

Sun A forms the root of everything that follows, depending on the yoga lineage your teacher hails from. The classic sequence I've learned from my first power yinyasa yoga teacher training includes Mountain Pose, Forward Fold, Halfway Lift, *Chaturanga*, Upward-Facing Dog, and Downward-Facing Dog. The repetition of these poses is an opportunity to prepare your body, your mind, and your breath and to practice *your* practice *within* a practice. In this way, you reignite everything you've learned.

In trauma alchemy, your Sun A, your first flow, is setting the most basic of self-care routines with ruthless persistence toward the intention you set earlier.

By reading this book, you've already begun to empower and uplift yourself. Most people have ideas and dreams, but too many of us are told all our lives, "Don't waste your time. Don't waste your energy. Be practical and realistic instead. Be safe."

But that's not you anymore. Ruthless persistence to achieve growth is how you go after what you want. Remember the distilled, personal intention that you journaled based on the previous chapter? That's where you need to focus. That's what you practice and intend during your first flow.

The Sanskrit word for *flow*, *vinyasa*, translates better into English and with greater meaning as "to place in a special way." And what you're placing in a special way is your intention in your everyday life.

As you may have experienced before, if you're consistent with your practice, you begin to feel calmer, more grounded, and lighter as you experience freedom from pain and anxiety. That is what true growth feels like, and like your yoga practice, it involves persistent repetition. The more persistent you are, the more you can tap into this feeling faster when you need it, on and off the mat.

The Way of Ruthless Persistence

So what do I mean by *ruthless persistence*? And how do you achieve it? First, let's discuss what ruthless persistence is not.

As I mentioned earlier, I had burned myself out from taking on too many responsibilities as a solo entrepreneur. The last decade has seen a major shift toward hustle culture and pushing yourself to the extreme, even at the cost of your health, your relationships, and yourself.

I lived that life. And at times, pushing yourself harder and moving out of balance is OK. But when it's a constant and it's causing more harm than good, it becomes a problem.

That's the issue with hustle culture: It's a way to compensate for the need to be in control and the fear of delegating. It's a coping mechanism for people who think no one can do a particular job as well as they can. And this coping strategy tends to be self-limiting.

At one point in time, I believed nobody could run aspects of my business as well as me. Hustle culture promotes doing everything yourself and grinding all hours of the day, which is exactly what I did. What happened to me? I fell apart and had to quit temporarily. And because everything was on my shoulders, it all crashed down when my mental health couldn't take it anymore.

That's not ruthless persistence. That's fear of healthy risk. Ruthless persistence instead is practice with consistency and sustainability. You may have heard me say before, "The strongest yogis know when to modify." If you're pushing yourself too hard, sooner or later, you're going to crash. And that's neither a good business model nor a strong yoga practice. It's not a healthy way to live your life, either. It's just not sustainable.

Instead, you achieve ruthless persistence through *having a routine*. Creating a consistent plan for each day keeps you persistent and lets you be ruthless about it because you aren't burning yourself out riding waves of emotional and physical highs and lows. Your routine isn't about focusing on should's and expectations. It's about being driven by your highest intention and values.

It may sound simple, boring, or less sexy than being a big-shot hustler, but it works. And let me tell you, there's nothing sexy about working nonstop in your pj's next to empty bags of chips and having no idea what time of day it is.

Every time I hire somebody for SarahBethYoga, I give them a crash course on how to work from home. You may be surprised how often people feel lost without the nine-to-five giving them structure and routine, so here is the most important tip: When it comes to routine-building, morning and evening routines are strongest. That's where you want to place your intention-based habits.

Mornings are great for setting habits because starting your day with achievement gets the momentum ball rolling first thing. This is where parts of the book *Atomic Habits: An Easy & Proven Way to Build Good Habits & Break Bad Ones* are helpful. The point is to make your habits easy and visible, and set yourself up for success by making your environment support them.

Want to make yoga part of your morning routine? Give your yoga mat a permanent spot next to your bed, download your videos in advance, and wear pj's you can practice in. Want to start a skin-care routine? Keep the products on your counter so they're accessible with ease.

When it comes to creating routines, less is more. That's most true when you're in the process of healing. Examine your routine, then remove anything you feel immediate resistance to, as well as anything that comes from outside expectations. You can always add more of your own steps later.

When you're dealing with stress and residual trauma, your self-care often suffers, and, if you're like me, your morning routine is completely nonexistent. Creating small daily habits is the first step toward taking back control and instilling the self-care you need and deserve.

Please understand that a routine will ebb and flow just as your life does. So be gentle with yourself if you're having a hard time, say, maintaining your spring routine into the summer. You might have more day-to-day family demands, less structure at work or school, and a different sleep schedule.

What should you do when your routine ebbs? You modify and establish a *new* routine! Tweak your habits until they fit with where you are so you can continue the healing process.

Let me share an example of what I call my bare-ass minimum (BAM) morning routine:

- Wake up
- Make bed
- Brush teeth
- Wash face
- Get dressed
- One to five minutes of breathing meditation (this item is the first to get removed/added, depending on how my mental health is)
- Make breakfast and get the kids ready for the day

See? Easy. However, in the pits of depression, this simple routine is not nearly BAM enough. So in that case, I would make it as BAM as it needs to be: Wake up, brush teeth, get dressed. Done. Then I would gradually add the rest as the habit got stronger.

When I was in hustle mode while running my business, I had no consistent routines. I would roll out of bed and trudge to the kitchen to help my kids get ready for school. I didn't brush my teeth, wash my face, or change out of my loose T-shirt and leggings. There was no motivation to wake up earlier.

I had high-functioning depression; I was living in fight-or-flight mode from unresolved childhood trauma. And that left me no time for self-care. My high productivity gave no clear sign of a problem, yet I was dragging myself around. I wasn't listening to my body. I sacrificed my self-care, my values, and my needs, and this led to burnout. My mental health spiraled so badly that I said, "Fuck it," and quit SarahBethYoga.

During the time I took off, I healed and reestablished my self-care habits. I asked myself, *What's the bare minimum I can do and still feel great?* That's when I started my BAM morning routine, and it helps me feel good every day. Even if I'm doing the bare minimum, I'm taking care of myself. That's the power of routine: Even a simple repetition of basic self-care habits provides you with certainty and security that helps you heal and adjust to your rest-and-relaxation nervous system.

Take your time here to set up your BAM routine if that's what you need in your healing journey: a BAM morning, a BAM evening, or a BAM feel-better routine for those days where you feel the funk. Whatever it is, create it with your intention in mind, then modify and tweak as you live your life. Once you have a routine established, then you're ready to move on to the next flow.

In the next chapter—the next flow—we're going to challenge the new routine. We're going to intentionally push beyond what's beginning to become comfortable. And it will be worth it. Because on the other side, you'll feel the strongest you've ever felt.

CHAPTER 6

SUN B—
WARRIOR FLOW

From the age of five, I suffered severe illness. My stomach hurt most of the time, leading to food anxiety, and I was always running to the bathroom with bloody bowel movements. Yet I kept it all a secret.

At the same time, my mom and I had a strained relationship. We both have strong personalities, so we quarreled all the time, and we had difficulty communicating due to cultural differences. My mom grew up in Africa and was raised with an authoritarian culture focused on obedience and control, whereas I was born and raised in the United States and grew up in an authoritative culture where I expected healthy boundaries and connection.

On top of that, my mom had full custody of me. When times were good, I saw my dad about half the time. But when times were bad, I lost access to him and the extracurricular activities I enjoyed, like piano and Girl Scouts. I was living two lives I couldn't control. And as I got older, the fights with my mom intensified.

At the age of nine, I was hospitalized and diagnosed with ulcerative colitis. In a way, the diagnosis made it worse. Now everyone else knew my secret, but I still had to take care of myself. Having to follow a strict diet, read nutrition labels, and keep track of all my medications and refills was overwhelming. I had already been in pain for years, and now I had immense responsibility, too.

In addition to the burden of this new diagnosis and what came with it, I was living like I was walking on eggshells. Something had to change. And something did, but nothing I wanted—or could have anticipated.

When I was twelve, my maternal grandmother passed away. She lived in the same neighborhood as my mom and I. She was an essential person in our family unit, and I spent most of my free time at her place. When she died, I grieved like I would have for a parent. I was alone, and I had lost my haven.

Within a couple of months, I googled the question, "How can I divorce my mom?" It wasn't that I had no compassion for her losing her mother. But I was shortsighted and felt the situation would only get worse unless I fixed it.

In the middle of another fight, I told my mom that I was going to emancipate myself. She called my dad. He was shocked and asked, "Are you sure you want to do this?"

I said yes. After all, my childhood was over in my eyes, and he said he would help me. A neighbor I had babysat for offered to be my attorney, pro bono. It's difficult to prove that a child of twelve is self-sustaining, so we switched from seeking emancipation to giving my dad custody. The case dragged on for two years. It was a hard time for everyone in the family. And by a hard time, I mean a dark pit measuring two years wide that nobody wants to go near again. Going to court was awful. We had to put the facts and our feelings out there in public, and everything was a battle.

My limited memory of those years made me question myself. It was hard to stand my ground and fight for my future. But after two years of court, my father received full custody. No longer was I living two lives I couldn't control. My father gave me full control over where I would stay, with my mom or with him, and when.

In the years after the court decision, my mom and I spoke only once. We had a giant blowup, and from ages fourteen to eighteen, I had no relationship with her. I also reunited with my ex-boyfriend during that time, replacing one dysfunctional, abusive relationship with another. Just like my mom and I, my ex and I played the roles of the controller and the control. It took another four years to free myself.

Meeting those challenges required me to adopt the mindset of a warrior. Let's discuss how yoga promotes that frame of mind.

How Heat Brings Healing

In a yoga session, Sun Salutation B, or Sun B, is the second flow. Like Sun A, it's about practicing repetition. But it's heat-building, and it challenges you on your mat and in your breath. You put yourself in Warrior Poses, like Warrior 1 and Warrior 2. In the second flow, your heart pounds. It's exhilarating and, at times, intense.

Sun B is a peak endurance and strength challenge. It's also when you feel your strongest. That's because you've practiced everything that has led you to this moment. You must approach these obstacles with strength. This is true growth.

At this point in *Trauma Alchemy*, you know your intention, your priorities, which old patterns you've had to disrupt, and which old beliefs you've replaced. You've established your BAM routine, and now it's time to act. The next step is defining and practicing the Sun B of your trauma alchemy.

What are the Warrior Poses that make up your Sun B? What would take your journey to the next level? For some, the answer is daily yoga, meditation, or hiring a qualified therapist. For others, it's sitting down and having a hard conversation you've been putting off for years. Maybe that's telling your spouse about an adverse childhood experience or a past abusive relationship that would explain a lot of your current relationship problems and miscommunications.

Your Sun B practice may include self-love and improving your body image. If that's the case, you may want to add this to your daily routine: Stand in front of your mirror, and speak positively to and about yourself out loud. "Girrrrl, your legs are fine! You look great in that dress! Purple is a good color for you. It brings out your beautiful eyes." It may feel awkward and unfamiliar at first to hype yourself up, but soon, you'll notice that it feels pretty good. Over time, with repetition, you'll build confidence. Trust the process. And remember, you can love yourself and be a work in progress at the same time.

You already know what your Sun B Warrior Pose is . . . and if you feel that you don't, then set this book down, close your eyes, and quiet your mind. Your answers will come to you.

So now let me ask you, what does your Sun B practice look like? What's the Warrior Pose or Poses that will challenge you and take you to the next level in your healing process? Write it down. Make it happen.

At this point in Sun B, you may be surprised by how much stronger you've gotten. You've shown you can break through the motivation cycle and show up for yourself. You trust yourself to feel good in the moment, learn the lesson, and know that your future self will be thankful.

Maybe you don't get on the mat thinking, *I'm gonna hit those Warriors today!* Just follow along, and you'll find yourself in those poses. That's because of your practice. Through that practice—through repetition—it gets easier and easier. You train yourself to break through the motivation cycle by just doing it.

In moments of challenge, you may be subject to self-distraction. It's easy to find distractions if you're looking for them. But it's in moments of challenge that you create calm in the chaos. You can practice this on the mat, shaking and sweating in Warrior Pose. You can also invoke that Warrior mindset off the mat by training yourself to go from reactive to responsive—especially when it's hard. What you practice on the mat reflects in your life off the mat and vice versa.

In Chapter 2, I shared how my mom and I built a new relationship. We didn't pick up where we had left off when I was sixteen. We built a new relationship as two adults with mutual respect, healthy boundaries, and a desire for growth, love, and connection. I don't believe we would have this relationship now had I not been a warrior for myself back then. My mom has also put in her own hard work, growing and taking her Warrior Poses over the past two decades since my childhood.

I had no idea I would ever have a good relationship with my mom. She and I both went through our own warrior journeys and met again as adults. For that, I'm so grateful.

Just as my challenges pushed me to the limit, Sun B kicks your butt. You're dripping with sweat, but that's when the endorphins kick in. As you get a drink of water, you feel good about yourself because you did it and you're now stronger for it.

CHAPTER 7

CORE SERIES

Until recently, I didn't remember anything from my childhood. All I knew was that at some point I developed ulcerative colitis and I had a tumultuous relationship with my mom. Seven years of my childhood— my life from five to twelve—were a total blur.

Although I remembered almost nothing from my childhood, there was one thing I knew for certain: I had unresolved childhood trauma, and for most of my life, I blamed my mom. I could feel it in my body. Resentment and anger were directed at her, but I didn't have the memories in my head to match the pain. After six years of therapy, it took one tool to unlock the memories I'm sharing with you.

Many years ago, the therapist I saw for postpartum anxiety and depression encouraged me to try something called eye movement desensitization and reprocessing (EMDR). But I was afraid it would open an emotional can of worms I wasn't ready for, so I turned that opportunity down.

Then my last therapist, who happened to be a psychiatrist, diagnosed me with CPTSD. I agreed with the diagnosis after some research showed that it exactly described my experience. But how could I move forward? How could I heal if I didn't know the cause? I had been through years of therapy, and although it had helped my life in the present, I still had no memories of my past. I had no idea what to do with the diagnosis.

But a new option presented itself: ketamine. I only knew about ketamine, or Special K, as a club drug, and I was not interested in recreational drug use or partying. I'm a wife, mother, and entrepreneur; not a raver, and I am definitely not looking to get high.

Then I found out that ketamine infusions, done in a monitored, clinical environment, stimulates episodic memory while preventing emotional attachment, so the experiences are not retraumatizing. Ketamine has also been used to treat injured Vietnam War vets and people experiencing severe depression and suicidal thoughts.

Learning about ketamine treatments piqued my curiosity and opened my mind. I'm no stranger to the life-changing benefits of psychedelics, but since becoming a mother, I wasn't comfortable with the idea of exploring those again. The prospect of this treatment option being offered within a professional setting gave me the safety and security I needed to face my childhood memories. I took the leap and booked six sessions (each running forty-five minutes) over three weeks.

By the fourth session using ketamine, I remembered my entire childhood. Every fragmented memory returned in a complete timeline. After that, I went home and journaled for hours about my childhood. I wrote about the constant fighting, the moving between two homes, hiding the pain of my ulcerative colitis and being my own caretaker, and the two-year court battle to become emancipated from my mom

Journaling all this and revealing how living with an undiagnosed, severe chronic illness dominated my childhood that was already in turmoil, with the added drama of family fights and courtroom struggles, was a cathartic experience that left me a sobbing mess. I wasn't crying because I was retraumatized. I was crying for the little girl who experienced all that and also what she didn't get to experience. I felt sorrow and compassion for myself. I finally saw what I had repressed, and that release needed to happen. It didn't serve me to bottle those emotions anymore. It was intense, and I knew it was a breakthrough for me.

That intensity resembled the core series in yoga, like Boat Pose, Plank, Side Plank, and Crow Pose. They challenge you in the most intense way mentally and physically. It looks easy, but you may not be able to hold a pose for more than a few seconds. It's humbling. And the more you put yourself in that humbling position, the longer you're able to do it, and with good form.

This is when you need to let go of everything else, feel the heat, and just endure it. Stoke the fire. Burn the dead wood. Slough off what you don't need so you can grow anew. Think of controlled burns. If you want a flourishing forest, you have to clear the path of dead debris blocking your growth.

And the core series aligns with trauma alchemy. This is about facing the deepest, most wounded parts of yourself. It's looking in the mirror at your own reflection as if it were you as a child.

This is also known as inner-child work. The inner child is not just a metaphorical way to describe the effects of a significant childhood experience that linger long into adulthood. The inner child is a studiable phenomenon that exists within your body and your mind. In clinical hypnosis therapy, certified practitioners understand that working with a patient's subconscious mind means speaking to the individual's inner child.

From birth, the subconscious mind grows and matures along with the waking mind. It's informed by all the beliefs, ideas, and knowledge we gain. But the subconscious mind reaches its peak around age five or six. So your greatest desires and fears are all formed during this time in childhood.

In other words, your subconscious is you as a five-year-old. That's your inner child, and that's who you are going to meet in the heat of the core series. It's just you and that version of you. You may have heard of it before, and maybe you're skeptical. But it's a transformative practice. It's about re-parenting your inner child when it's just the two of you in the heat of the moment. I invite you to do this trauma alchemy core series multiple times.

When I first began doing inner-child work, I asked myself, "Where should I start? How old is my inner child?" I saw her at six years old, right about at the beginning of those repressed memories.

Here's a good way to start: Find a picture of yourself at five or six to better visualize that child. Imagine that child is alive and well, doing all the same things that served you then. Your adult self looks like a stranger to your inner child. So you need to create a new relationship. And how do five-year-olds build connections? Through play. Through relationship-building, you can allow your inner child to trust you.

I took that picture of myself, put it on my phone, meditated on it, and set an intention to meet her. That's what I did in ketamine therapy. During one of my sessions, I found myself on an old playground—one that I had played on at that age. I saw my inner child playing, and I played in parallel. We created a relationship. When I ran to my mom's house, she hesitated.

"I'll take care of you," I said, reaching out. That was all she ever needed to hear—a safe, responsible adult saying, "I'll take care of you." She took my hand, and that was the beginning of re-parenting myself, work that has made me a better parent to my own children.

In the first few weeks of beginning my inner-child work, I noticed my chest tightened in a fight-or-flight response as a reaction to an argument I had with Leland. So I told my inner child, "It's OK for adults to argue. It doesn't mean he's going to leave you or hurt you. Adults can argue and still love each other. You're OK. I'll take care of you."

Why did I have that reaction? Because as a child, most arguments resulted in a full-blown war. I realized that peaceful, even though uncomfortable, disagreement is the mark of a healthy relationship.

Your inner child aka subconscious mind is the seat of your long-term memories, habits, and so on. Deep breathing returns your focus to the present. Practicing deep breathing has helped me have mature arguments without blowing up. A deep breath helps me sit in discomfort and allow strong emotions to process and eventually release. Breath is what makes yoga, yoga.

Most people don't breathe deeply or mindfully throughout the day. That's why so many love yoga and so many others find it that much harder to quit smoking cigarettes! I smoked from the ages of eighteen to twenty and replaced my smoke breaks with deep-breathing breaks, along with neuro linguistic programming, to help me quit. Wouldn't we all benefit from a breath break when we're stressed?

Once you make it through the heat to the other side, with your breath as your tool to stay grounded and your re-parenting self-talk, you'll stay in control even when your inner child wants to take over. That applies on the mat and in real life. You can remind yourself through your self-talk, "We are strong. We can do this. We were made to do hard things."

But it's not just about re-parenting your inner child. Inner-child work also involves letting that little one come out to play. Stomp in the puddles, watch the butterflies, sit in the grass, pick up long-lost interests, and make it your inner child's job to play and have fun, not to worry about how to take care of you. The adult version of you has that under control, remember? "I'll take care of you."

Even after this book and your trauma alchemy journey concludes, your inner-child work will continue with ongoing re-parenting, self-talk, and plenty of play.

Bring Your Inner Child to the Mat

So how do you meet your inner child and invite him/her into your yoga practice? Through levity, lightness, and play.

Let's take the Crow Pose, for example. If you've ever attempted it, you may recall placing your hands on the ground with your hips in the air and your knees resting on your triceps as you bend your elbows and try to lift your feet. You may also recall that this pose is really challenging and beating yourself up about not being able to lift your feet yet only makes the pose feel harder. It's when you approach it with play and a little smile that you feel some lightness in the pose, and you remember that it's not about getting your feet up but enjoying the exploration on your way there.

On and off your mat, focus, take deep breaths, and enjoy the whole experience. There's no need to be so serious all the time. Seriousness can weigh you down. Instead, when you lose your balance, laugh with yourself because levity gives you the grace you need to fly.

Consider the alternative: telling your inner child the discouraging criticism you may have adopted in your self-talk. You wouldn't tell a five-year-old trying the Crow Pose, "You suck. You'll never do it right! Just stop trying." No, you would use a light, constructive touch with a child.

The childhood trauma I experienced affected me greatly as an adult, and in some ways I'm still peeling back layers. If your negative childhood experiences or traumas are still affecting you, there are many methods to help you break through, such as hypnosis, trauma-focused therapy, EMDR, and clinical ketamine treatments.

At this point in your practice, you've met your inner child and formed a connection. In the next stage of trauma alchemy, you'll realize you survived all the past intense experiences together.

CHAPTER 8

BALANCE

Remember my first yoga class? I was a teenager in a room full of adults, a beginner on the mat surrounded by expert yogis, a gangly, awkward kid who fell over every few poses while everyone else stood strong.

Worst of all, they made it look easy. In most yoga sessions, the balance stage follows the core series. Longer stretches are held, balance is focused, and little movement is made. This part is challenging, both to body and mind.

In my first yoga class, I swayed side to side trying to hold the balance poses. I overcompensated when I lost my footing. It was embarrassing, but I didn't quit. I kept up this practice. Over the next few years, I stopped falling and looked as balanced and graceful as the others from that first class. I never would've gotten where I am today as a yogi—or as an entrepreneur, a yoga teacher, a wife, and a mother—if I had quit when I felt off-balance, unsupported, or lost.

Sometimes, during this trauma alchemy journey, you may feel like you've messed up or taken two steps back. Those low moments when you're forced to hold the posture of balance are part of the process. And experiencing it is progress.

Think about how a pendulum swings. At first, it goes back and forth, furiously unbalanced. But then the movements become smaller and more controlled. It's the same in your practice. Your balance and control become more precise, and you move beyond self-doubt into self-belief.

Finding your balance doesn't mean you will be perfect. It means the pendulum swings will not be so extreme. When you see someone who's balanced next to someone who's unbalanced, the former remains calm and centered while making micro-adjustments to hold the pose, while the latter struggles to maintain control, body, and mind.

Life, and your trauma alchemy practice, can be the same way, stirring up self-doubt any time you stumble or fall. But it's OK because this is a practice, not a perfect.

So you'll want to be mindful about how you react. What you don't want to do is fall off-balance and never get up again. If you do fall, it doesn't mean you can't balance, but that you need to get up and try again, perhaps this time with a modification so you can ease into your balance practice.

I don't tell beginners to do the most advanced version of Tree Pose. Instead I bring them into a variation that involves placing their heel on their standing ankle. So they have one foot fully on the ground and the toes of their other foot on the ground while their knee bends open. When you start there, you experience how it feels to have both feet stable in a stronger, more balanced pose starting from the ground up. Each time you return there, you can take it a little further, knowing you can always bring your toes back down to the floor to catch yourself.

You'll notice that what happens when you do balancing poses correlates to real-life challenges. That's the point of this book. Whenever you do yoga, you will think about how your practice on the mat connects to what you do off it. You'll realize you're not just doing Tree Pose, you're doing something that's pushing you to grow in all areas of your life.

On the other hand, you may have read inspirational books like this before and come away thinking, *Sounds great, but how does it apply to my life?*

Everyone's circumstances are unique. This book gives you the tools to do this work in your life now. Know that you'll fall and fail at times, but the strongest yogis know they'll always get back up. You emerge from self-doubt by balancing a little longer each time than you're used to, even in a pose that doesn't feel 100 percent comfortable.

When you hold a pose you're new to, like tree, it is natural to sway, spread your arms, and move your free leg to regain your balance. And it's easy to say, "I can't do it," and stop all-together, skipping the pose. It may be more comfortable, but that doesn't lead to growth. Because we only grow outside our comfort zone.

Putting yourself in unstable positions while in a safe environment gives your body and mind the chance to grow stronger, more connected, and more secure. Security comes from knowing you can take it one step at a time. That knowledge only comes when you begin to raise a leg off the floor.

As you continue to practice that pose, you can take it a little further each time. Maybe this time, you slide your foot farther up your calf while knowing you can place your toes back down as needed. It's OK to feel secure knowing you can catch yourself. You might teeter a little bit, but you can correct yourself and return to center. That's one of the biggest benefits of this practice.

But it only comes from stepping out of your comfort zone. So let's introduce an uncomfortable balancing pose for your off-the-mat trauma alchemy practice. It will have you feeling like you're raising a leg off the ground. You may feel unstable and insecure at first, but this exercise will help you develop more stable and secure relationships and more self-confidence.

Balancing the Past

This exercise involves uncomfortable conversations with the most important people in your life now. It is not advised to dig up people from your past, especially if those relationships were unhealthy or abusive in any way. This process is about asking for healthy emotional support from the people who know you well and may have known you in your past.

Discuss something you've repressed with a loved one in a nurturing environment where you can seek emotional support. Open with a simple question. For example, I asked my mom, dad, and brother, "How would you describe my childhood?"

I listened to their answers, which validated what I had already discovered. And then I explained what I had been through in my own trauma alchemy, which opened their eyes to what my experience felt like for me. "I never thought about it that way."

It not only allowed me to share my feelings, but it also gave others the chance to know and better understand me. And it helped me clear the air to form stronger relationships with those whom I love today. I no longer felt alienated or disconnected like I did before. Sometimes the people in our lives who have been around the longest have a past version of us stuck in their heads. This exercise helped replace the distance between who they thought I still was and who I am now with a newfound connection. That process brought my inner child healing.

This can be an incredibly challenging discussion, especially if it's to reveal a part of your past to a loved one or partner who didn't know what happened. Take your time, create a safe space, and tell the person that you want to have a "listening" conversation, not a "solutions" conversation, so that you can be heard. It may go well, where the other person will support you, love you, and listen to you, maybe even providing more insight from their own experience. It may also not go well, as the other person needs more time to process or do their own inner work. Let them go, and do your best not to take their reaction personally, as it is more of a reflection of their self-work than it is their perception of you. This is a very challenging balancing pose and may be the most uncomfortable. At the very least, do it for you so you can continue your growth and live your truth.

But what if you're unable to speak with the people you need to? Maybe they passed away, are long gone, beyond boundaries, or for whatever reason are inaccessible. Consider speaking with a qualified therapist, especially about past unhealthy relationships. It would not have been wise to ask my ex-boyfriend, "How would you describe dating me?" To deal with my trauma with him, I maintained my boundaries and worked with a therapist to experience forgiveness and understanding from a distance. That forgiveness allowed me to release the hold that relationship had on me so I could give myself fully to a new one.

Professional therapeutic advice can be superior in these situations. Friends just want you to feel happy, so they may tell you what's comfortable rather than what you need to hear. But therapists are trained to deal with these situations. Their job isn't just to help you feel better, but to push you toward growth so you can overcome the painful emotions weighing you down.

If you start talking to someone important to you but then realize, "Oh boy, I'm not ready for this," slow down and take it step by step. Return to the conversation when you're ready. The yoga equivalent would be slowly bringing your toes back down to the mat in your Tree Pose. Return to the more challenging variation when you're ready.

Use nonattachment as your balancing tool here. You can recall what happened, and you've already done it before with the movie theater exercise. You've been able to observe it all over again with yourself removed from the scene. When you're talking to others, ask them how they would describe your childhood, or at least the formative years that they witnessed. Hearing their perspective will give you insight and validation. And if you choose to reveal what you've discovered, explain it to them movie-theater style, without emotional attachment. What has passed can stay in the past, even when you shine light on it in the present.

Even with all the monk-equivalent work of nonattachment, dredging up the past can still create emotional experiences. Listen to your body. If you feel your chest tightening, your jaw clenching, or other physical sensations of different emotions arising, that may be a sign for you to end the conversation or change the subject. You could say, "Hey, let's revisit this topic in a few days. I've got some thinking to do."

Healing may not require the people who were in your life then to be in your life now. There's also something to be said for shared trauma. Think of therapy and support groups for people who've gone through a similar experience. You're not the common denominator, and what happened isn't your fault.

For example, I developed a friendship with my ex-boyfriend's ex-girlfriend. I gained immense healing from talking to her. Before, I second-guessed myself time and again about that relationship. I wondered if what happened between us—what he did to me—was really all my fault. But we both realized we were the kind of broken young women he preyed on. It wasn't *us*; it was *him*. He was an angry and controlling man. He was the common denominator.

I also joined group therapy for postpartum depression with other mothers my age. That experience gave me context and gratitude. And it opened my world beyond my experience. Your therapist may be able to do the same, perhaps even refer you to a support group.

Listening to others' experiences helps you realize you're not alone and that there is a silver lining to your trauma. You can feel grateful for your unique struggles, and you can provide support. Those realizations also take the focus off you.

Nurturing someone else is, in a sense, nurturing yourself—perhaps your inner child. Think about it: how long can you tell others to forgive themselves before you forgive yourself? And it just so happens that forgiveness is our next flow.

CHAPTER 9

DEEP STRETCHING

Content Warning: The next few pages are an intense recount of a domestic violence situation that was a catalyst for me in my life. It also introduces an essential lesson for this chapter. If you would like to skip this content, feel free to go to Chapter 10.

Have you ever held on to a relationship too long? It's like a fruit or vegetable at the back of the refrigerator. Yeah, the one from a few grocery trips ago. You get to the point where you worry it will grow mold and assume it already has. So there it stays where it has been. *Maybe one of these days, I'll do something about it,* you tell yourself.

So it can be with our relationships. For whatever reason, the bond has weakened; the connection is no longer mutually beneficial, or perhaps it has become toxic, festering with mold. But one or both parties hang on to it, like we tend to do with that single cucumber in the fridge or that last ultra-ripe banana in the pantry. Then there comes a point where it's too late to *not* do anything about it.

That was me as a teenager.

Regarding that abusive relationship I was in as a teenager, I said that I eventually ended it and found the man who is now my husband.

But I didn't really give you any details, and it feels like I glossed over that part of my life. So let me tell you a bit more and set the scene for what happened.

During this time, I had *just* liberated myself from the abusive, dysfunctional relationship I had with my mom. I was fourteen years old, freshly out of court from that family divorce. I now lived at my dad's house full time. I switched schools and, within a couple of weeks, met this boyfriend simply due to proximity. We lived near each other since I had moved and often saw each other walking to and from school. It was a whirlwind, to put it mildly.

Yes, I had gotten through these issues with my family, I felt I was finally in control of my life, and it was changing rapidly. But this new boy was full of red flags from the very beginning. Yet I didn't see them. I *couldn't* see any of them because all his red flags seemed so familiar to the point that I actually gravitated toward them. He initially felt like home because what I had known as love and affection were really forms of control, drama, and abuse. He was serving the same meal I had been fed my whole life, and I didn't know any better—except this meal would turn out to be much worse than anything I had swallowed before.

I was a teenager, so I felt like an adult in many ways. And, like most teens, I felt misunderstood and confused. Add on the unresolved traumas from my childhood, and I can see now why I walked away from one unhealthy relationship right into another. And that relationship went sour at an alarming speed. He was possessive, controlling, and jealous from the start. Within a couple of weeks, he was pinching my side to maintain his control while he seethed with rage at me through his teeth in the hallways of our high school. This evolved into fights over the clothing I wore, with shirts and shorts being ripped off and destroyed, or about the people I spoke to. Nothing and no one was safe. I learned to look at the ground, avoid conversations with other boys, and not to say the "wrong" things so that I wouldn't anger him.

Over the course of four years, the abuse always pushed the edge of the last incident, leading to near daily occurrences of getting hit in the face or body with fists, kicked in the ribs, choked, or pinned against walls while the boy I loved morphed into a blind-rage of a person I didn't want to believe was also him. It was absolutely a Jekyll & Hyde situation that left me with emotional trauma and neurological damage called silent ocular migraines from getting hit so many times in the head. What people saw as a charming boy with a short fuse was really an uncontrolled, abusive, and destructive young man.

We already talked earlier in the book about the patterns I uncovered in this relationship, but I didn't tell you the conclusion to that story. So let me tell you how it ended.

Two weeks before college began, I decided it was over—suddenly and forever. A switch flipped in me, and there was no returning to what had been before. One moment, I just knew that someday I would meet someone whom I would have a healthy, happy family with, and this someone wasn't him. I fully realized that, if I wanted the future that included motherhood and a loving relationship, this guy was not going to be a part of it, and I had to remove every aspect of him from my life, period. The fantasy of a different life would never come true and could never be fully realized unless I ended *this* relationship—and all the dysfunction that came with it—permanently.

So two weeks before college, I pulled up to his house in my car, and at first, we broke up in the car. By "we," I mean I told him it was over. This was nothing new, and we had repeated this song and dance a dozen times before. We started arguing, and I decided I would just get my stuff from his house; I even left the car running. And when we walked inside, he locked me in his parents' house for the next three hours.

As soon as we entered the house, he dead-bolted the door and put the keys in his pocket. It was like he instinctively knew this time was different, that I was serious, and I knew he wasn't playing, either. This was it.

I instantly knew I needed to de-escalate the situation, but it was too late. He went into a blackout rage. All I remember is fists flying and veins popping from his face and neck. There was no reasoning with him. *He was gone.* I was so done with the relationship, and he couldn't emotionally hurt me anymore, so he resorted to physical violence. He started grabbing and throwing me, hitting and biting me. He tried to pull my fingers back like he was trying to break them. At one point, he tried to break my arm.

I went numb. My nervous system reaction, I later learned, happened because I could not flee or fight or fawn, so I froze. I remembered his parents were out of town, and my dad likely had seen my car outside of his house and thought nothing of it since my car was often parked there. It would be days before anyone would know that I was there or even to think that something was wrong and maybe that they should check on me.

No one was coming to save me.

It was, legally, a kidnapping.

He was kidnapping me.

I ran for my phone, but it was in my car, which was still running outside. So I went for the landline, but he ripped the cord out of the wall.

All the windows were slant-open windows. *Do I break a window?* I felt bad about the idea of damaging his family's property and the fact that I didn't have any money to pay for a broken window. But he was becoming more and more violent, so I needed to try to calm him down. I started to turn on my fawning response and butter him up a little bit. I acted really sweet and calm, and I said I was sorry and that we shouldn't break up.

"I'm really hurting; I could use an ice pack," I told him. "Can you just give me time alone upstairs?" I pleaded.

There was an attic in the house, which was his brother's bedroom, and I remembered it had an octagonal window. At that point, I was willing to climb out of the attic window to escape. I tried to get him to go to the kitchen and get away from me so I could go upstairs. He had calmed down by that point and was being sweet. He said, "I love you so much. And you know, I wanna be together forever, and you don't deserve this. We shouldn't fight like this."

At one time, I would've eaten all that up, but we were past the point of no return. I was numb, and I was doing whatever I could to get myself out of this situation because *I was done*—with him, with everything.

At some point, I finally made it upstairs alone, walked toward the window, and noticed a flip phone on the floor. I immediately grabbed it and shoved it in my bra. I knew I could use any phone to call 911. I could hear him coming back up the stairs, so I began acting more vulnerable and scared and hurting to bargain for more alone time.

"Please get me an ice pack, and let's be together," I told him. That's what he wanted to hear. He then brought me to his bedroom, which was all the way down in the basement. I was so numb at this point that I wasn't even talking. He started tucking me in his bed, and he finally agreed to get me an ice pack.

The second he was out of earshot, I yanked that phone out of my bra and turned it on—*Oh my God! It turned on!*

Panicked, I called 911. *It's ringing.*

"What's your emergency?"

"Help! I am trapped at this address, and my ex-boyfriend has locked the doors. I can't get out! He's beating me up!"

Suddenly, I heard a noise—he had heard me on the phone. He flew down the stairs, ran to me, ripped the phone from my hand, and broke it in half over his legs.

I looked at him and said, "You messed up. *Now* they're coming; they're on their way."

He crumpled to the floor. He buried his head in his knees and started crying.

"What did you just do? What did you do?"

"It's over," I said.

It felt like barely a minute had passed between the phone call and police kicking the back door down. Once they did, they called out for me, and I emerged from the dark shadows of that basement for the last time. They pulled him out and put him in handcuffs, and then they started taking pictures of all my bruises. I had open-wound claw marks down both of my arms from his fingernails. I had marks on my face and bruises on my arms. My clothes and my purse were all ripped. The inside of the house looked like a disaster zone. It was clear what had happened.

I started giving my story. "Do you want to press charges?" I was asked.

That was the moment where I decided this was never going to happen again. "Yes, I will press charges."

Two weeks later, I was sitting in college orientation. During that time, his dad called me over and over, begging me to stop pressing charges, telling me I was ruining his son's life. I realized his son needed the boundaries of a felony and to experience the repercussions of domestic violence so that he would never do this again. It had been clear from the beginning that this kid had a serious anger problem. The day I had met him, he had told me that he was grounded because he had thrown a chair through his kitchen window. At the time, such an obvious red flag looked green to me. But I could tell this wasn't a problem because of me, and I didn't want anyone else to experience it.

Yet even after I escaped that situation, it wasn't really over. I was in my college orientation dealing with actual PTSD, not knowing how I was going to be able to function or catch up with everyone else. After a few weeks there and seriously struggling, I ended up calling a suicide hotline. That suicide hotline sent me to rehab in Florida. I decided that if that was what was going to help me heal, I needed to do it. So I took it.

The sobriety helped, as did the intense amount of individual and group therapy. And in that year after I returned from rehab, which was twelve weeks long, I had to go testify against my ex-boyfriend. So I was really going forward with it, but my life was still spiraling.

That entire next year after I called the police, I was way out of my comfort zone, stretching myself away from what was comfortable, which was him and the abuse. I could have easily gone back at any point. I could have called him or dropped the charges. But I continued to pursue all of it. I knew that rehab for substance abuse wasn't the right thing for me, but it was better than not doing anything. I needed therapy and a supportive place to process and heal. So I approached the process like abuse was my addiction.

The craziest thing is, I met my now husband a week into college—three weeks after the kidnapping. I still had scabs and faint bruises on my arms. I felt so strongly that this was the guy I wanted to have kids with, but I knew I needed time to heal from everything that had happened, and I didn't want to jump into another relationship. We instantly magnetized to each other and spent most of our time together for those first few weeks, but then I disappeared when I left for rehab, and we didn't see each other again for another nine months. Miraculously, we got back together, and the rest is history.

I was trying to process and heal all of this without dependence on anyone else when my entire life prior to that was dependent on those abusive relationships and my identity was so wrapped up in the roles that

I had played in them. This was the first time where I was alone and not having anyone tell me who I was or how I should act or what I should do. I felt like a baby deer walking for the first time, trying to figure things out.

Part of figuring things out was that I had to forgive without closure. I had to release the resentment, experience the grief, and forgive the situation, myself, and the abuser without forgetting or minimizing it.

When you don't forgive, guilt and shame lingers. You end up resorting to false fixes and distractions like substances or partying. Support in the rehab center gave me the beginning of healing.

Then I had to learn how to move forward without closure. In other words, I had to forgive without contacting him. I had to trust that I could experience forgiveness without forgetting or minimizing what had happened. There was a lot of trauma that took a very long time for me to work through, but if I had never begun the work to process it all, I would likely be right back in that same situation today.

Your limbic system, your emotional brain, doesn't have a calendar. It doesn't have a clock. It doesn't know the difference between then, now, or the future. So your subconscious is always trying to resolve the trauma. And it's either punishing you with guilt and shame, distracting from or avoiding the trauma entirely, or it's going to try to fix it. And without a new perspective, a fresh set of eyes, or curiosity like the movie theater exercise, sometimes your brain will cause you to do something called repetition compulsion, an unconscious need to reenact early traumas so that you can "fix" them. That means returning to that situation, even if it's with a different person or a whole different situation—which is what I did by going from my relationship with my mother to the one with my ex-boyfriend.

But I had a major realization recently, and it's quite poetic: I went from my mom's house with glass walls to my dad's house that had illusionary walls—there was no protection and no real boundaries at that house. I literally walked through those walls, right to another abuser, at the age of fourteen. So I didn't have the therapy or the support or the processing or the healing or even a chance of any of that because I still had those patterns playing on repeat in my subconscious.

So how do you break through?

Stretching into New Seasons

In yoga, the next stage after balance poses is deep stretching, specifically deep hip openers. Most people's posture is curled up from sitting like little gremlins all day. Deep hip openers free your joints, muscles, ligaments, and bones from the effects of postures you've held too long that don't serve you anymore.

When you're suppressing emotions, it can result in tension in your body, especially your hips. And doing deep hip openers like Half Pigeon and Figure Four gives you space to process those emotions, allowing them to bubble up to the surface. This is the time when you need to really *feel* what's coming up. You have to let all these feelings move through you first in order to let them go.

Off the mat, the counterpart to deep stretching in trauma alchemy is forgiveness. That means forgiving the perpetrator, the situation, the bystanders, and of course, yourself. That's an important lesson I learned from experience.

Forgiveness is like the deep stretch in that you release *all* your emotional tension: built-up resentment, the desire for revenge, defensiveness, the need to feel justified, and anxiety over being ostracized. Forgiveness, combined with deep stretching, stops you from being embroiled in all that drama. Unless you remove that poison from your mind and body, it will destroy you.

Keeping tension locked in your hips can cause irreversible damage as you age. Early arthritis, limited movement, lower energy, and chronic pain can all develop. You end up overcompensating with other muscles and joints that become overworked and overstressed.

When you hold a grudge, it manifests when you interact with people you love. It's difficult to *not* lash out at someone innocent when you're fantasizing about hurting the person who hurt you. Imaginary fights in your mind set the tone for your perspective, your mood, your movement, and even your blood pressure and heart rate. Your body can't tell the difference between a real argument and an imaginary one with someone you haven't spoken to in years.

Forgiveness doesn't require you to speak to the other person, and in some cases, it's harmful to make contact again. Seeking an apology from my ex-boyfriend would have been physically and emotionally dangerous. As I said in the previous chapter, it's crucial to maintain your boundaries.

It's *you* who needs to dump the poison. Throwing acid at people who wronged you may get you burned. Treat a past abuser like an addictive substance. You don't need to relapse.

How to Forgive but Not Forget

Have a dedicated time to sit in a comfortable and safe space, alone. Think about the feeling, the situation, and the person. Notice any emotional attachment as you begin thinking. Those emotions are what must be processed. Sit with the discomfort without using your first coping strategy, like changing your thoughts, grabbing your phone, or running a revenge fantasy through your head.

Let the tension work itself out and dissipate. Pushing it down only locks it deeper inside you, and you'll eventually explode. Let it work through you by sitting in the discomfort and feeling the emotion. Perhaps this involves crying, screaming, journaling, verbalizing, tearing up paper, or throwing pillows. It's likely not going to be pretty or comfortable. As long as you don't hurt yourself or anybody else, then let it out. As the emotions rise and release, they'll dissipate in their intensity and cease to have control over you.

On the flip side, it's helpful to focus on positive results from the traumas you have experienced—the silver lining, so to speak. Ask yourself some questions: What are you grateful for after everything that has happened to you? Is there an upside to your pain? What lessons have you learned from your negative experiences?

Forgiveness does not mean admission of guilt or wrongdoing. It is not a martyr ploy to sit in shame or take the blame. It's also not saying that what happened was OK. It is simply putting down the poison and no longer carrying the emotional, mental, and physical burden of unprocessed pain.

As Joe Dispenza, an international lecturer and doctor of chiropractic care, says, "Memory without emotional attachment is wisdom."

If you feel strong emotions, self-blame, guilt, or shame, return to the movie theater exercise to detach and be neutral. That exercise helped me view my relationship from my ex's perspective. It was clear he was not well and had issues from the beginning. Who knows how he was raised and the abuse he might have suffered. Although what he did was wrong and I don't regret how I handled the situation, I was able to see that although he was trying to love me in his own way, which was dysfunctional and damaging, he was suffering within the prison of his own mind. He was never content or at peace. He was always angry, paranoid, distrusting, and so emotionally immature that violence was his only way to experience power and control. But I, too, was dysfunctional and damaged, and I enabled and allowed his behavior until I finally stopped.

Completing the process of forgiveness changed my life for the better. It has, along with all the work I've done, allowed me to view him as a flawed human being who was hurting at the time. And it finally allowed me to forgive completely and to close that dark chapter in my life while focusing on this new one, fresh and unburdened by any old feelings. He didn't have the emotional capacity to be mature then, so he did the best he knew how at the time. It doesn't mean it was OK. But it allowed me to experience forgiveness from a more neutral position. I let the memories from those four years rest in the past. I even thanked them KonMari style, so I no longer carry them with me. There's no longer any tension—or poison—in my hips.

During a yoga session, as you release tension from your hips during the deep stretches, emotional tension may arise. The key here is to feel it, sit in the discomfort, look right at it, and allow yourself to express it. After the tears fall or the inner wounds are felt, the tension eases, and you will feel relaxed and lighter—like emotional weights are lifting from your body. It's a *cathartic* experience. You're now relaxed and calm, and you feel your heart rate slowing down. It's the perfect preparation for the next stage of the journey.

CHAPTER 10

COOL DOWN

Do you remember playing connect the dots as a kid? Those puzzles with numbered dots, and you would connect each dot in sequence by drawing lines between them to form a complete image at the end?

You might call connecting the dots the theme of this chapter. Your every choice makes up part of a cause-and-effect relationship. So think of each decision or big event in your life as a dot. And when you connect the dots, you end up with a clearer picture of your life and why you are where you are today.

Yet we can only see the complete picture by looking at each past decision from the vantage point of the present. Hindsight gives you a bird's-eye view of your whole life. It gives you the perspective to take stock.

At first glance, the isolated dots seem to lack deeper meaning. Maybe your mind tries to impose order on the chaos, giving you a weird image.

Maybe your past does look like your mind's worst interpretation of the unfinished puzzle. You look back and think, *What a mess!* It may seem daunting, but it can be as simple as picking a place to start. Dot by dot, the big picture reveals itself.

Just like the connect-the-dots puzzle has you connecting the dots in numerological order, it's vital to connect each of your dots in chronological order to reveal the bigger picture. Then you can see the patterns in your decision-making, the silver lining behind the worst dots, and the gratitude in the connections between the dots.

Let's do a little connect-the-dots exercise with my life. Fighting with my mom led to my two-year court experience, which led to me switching schools because I moved in with my dad. And at my new school, I met my ex-boyfriend, whom I dated all through high school. While we were dating, I got admitted to a college near his so we could stay close. I still attended that college after severing ties with him, and that's where I met Leland.

That's the simple version. There may have been many more decisions that would form a more complete picture. Yet just connecting a few dots in my life illustrates the value of this activity. Notice how each experience was a point that led me to the future I wanted. And each experience was linked in a chain of cause and effect. That's why this activity involves connecting the dots to a narrative of your life.

In my example, connecting the dots formed the beautiful family I always wanted. All those events were necessary to create the final picture. If I'd missed even one, I would be somewhere else right now. Even the abusive relationship I had with my ex-boyfriend led me to the far different man I would marry.

Since removing even one piece of the puzzle would leave it incomplete or could have led to a different direction, you can't say life would be better if you had erased one dot. Each experience forms part of the journey toward your final destination, in some way or another.

And the activity continues. You are in a dot right now, but you can still have a vision for what you want in the future. I had a vision for what I wanted my final picture to look like, even though I didn't know how the dots would connect one day. Even if you're not where you want to be, you can look back at how the dots have lined up so far. And if you don't like where you are, you can always change direction, change your intention, set a goal, and focus on a different big picture. It's not too late to be who you want to be, just like it's never too late to change a yoga practice from one of frustration to one of peace. Trust that the complete picture will emerge in the end.

Begin the End

In a yoga session, the beginning of the end starts during the cooldown, a time of rest and reflection. Looking back at the dots of your practice so far, you've already done the work, repeated the flows, released the tension, challenged your muscles, and focused your mind. All the dots have lined up, so you are as ready as ever to just lie down relaxed to enjoy your cooldown stretches. You'll take a few minutes to just slow down, breathe, and feel good within a big twist, almost as if you're wringing water from a wet rag. This is the time to calm down, unwind, and release any other tension you've held on to throughout your practice.

Off the mat, you've come full circle as you've forgiven others and yourself, seeing your life and other people without emotional attachment. You've processed trauma and taken ownership of yourself, your emotions, and your reactions. Now you're connecting the dots of your practice, and your life, with an understanding and appreciation that it all led to here.

The yoga concept of *santosha* means "to be content with the now without needing anything more." I have the word tattooed on my Achilles tendon in Sanskrit as a reminder that I don't need anything to change to find happiness. I accept that everything that came before happened exactly as it was supposed to and that I'm exactly where I need to be in each and every moment.

Cool Off and Connect the Dots

Contemplate the connection between each dot of your life so far, and draw it out on paper giving each dot a little label and a number so you can keep track of the chronological order. When you get to your last dot, connect it with your first dot to create a full circle. It may look wonky and have edges, but that's OK. It's not supposed to be perfect.

As you connect each dot to the next, contemplate their connection, how each dot led to the next. Instead of getting caught up in any emotional high or low of any single dot, focus on the connections in between with gratitude and *santosha*. *Santosha* means "sitting and contemplating moments that mattered"—whether they were awful or highlights of your life—in a restful state. You're connecting the best *and* worst things that happened to you so you can see the bigger picture. If you feel emotions rising, let them through. Feel those emotions, then let them go, and shift to appreciation for everything that brought you where you are now: to a feeling of contentment, without wanting or needing anything more.

Connect your dots, then *accept your dots*. Complete acceptance embodies *santosha*. In doing so, you also find gratitude for your life story so far and for the picture being drawn, even if it's not the image you want to see yet. You have strength, resilience, growth, and self-love. You are in some way better than before.

That's not to say, "Thank God this awful thing happened." To echo what I said earlier, it's accepting your dots, and that each dot is part of the bigger picture that makes you who you are today.

Because all the dots, no matter how isolated they seem, are connected.

By the end of this chapter, you're feeling calm and content with the now, without needing anything more. You're living *santosha*. Now you're ready to conclude the sequence with the most important pose of all in yoga.

CHAPTER 11

SAVASANA

Why do people read books like this? And why do they read this far? Why practice yoga in the first place—or meditation, journaling, and therapy?

All these examples involve *inner work*. Reading a book might seem unrelated to practicing yoga or therapy, but each is a method to heal something inside of you and a quest to understand the self.

Peeling back the layers of who you are *not* reveals the true self beneath. It's a reinvention process. The trauma responses and coping strategies that once served you, but no longer do, are not you. You are not your intrusive thoughts; you are that spark deep down inside. That's your true self—full of love, light, and truth.

The place where your inner child resides is the place where both light and dark aspects of yourself exist. Embrace and nurture the love and positivity inside you. Tend to it like a garden, cultivate steady growth, and watch that side of you bloom. At the same time, you must shed the negative energy you're carrying. Cast it out and let it go completely. Reinvention requires *obsolescence*—making obsolete who you aren't.

My own trauma alchemy resulted in the shedding of fight or flight as my main operating system. That response system no longer served me. How could it? It was a subconscious response to protect me from an unsafe environment by keeping me in a vigilant state. But I'm no longer in an abusive environment, and I'm not ill anymore. I feel safe, healthy, and content.

That's how you'll feel near the end of a yoga session. After the cooldown, you lie flat on your back. You want all your muscles to be as loose as possible. Allow yourself to take up space. Relax and close your eyes. Soften each muscle in your body—from the biggest in your hips, thighs, and shoulders to the smallest around your eyes. Feel the tension melt away, and lie in complete and total relaxation, allowing your mind to settle into nothing.

This is *savasana*. In Sanskrit, it means "corpse pose." It's about going from sixty to zero. You've gone through a sequence to release the past from your mind and body—the old yogi has died, and the new yogi is alive. When you reach this point, you've come to the death of your old self.

At the same time, it's a state of complete relaxation where you get to just *be*. It's a moment of lying in complete stillness when you're making the choice to be reborn. After my six ketamine sessions, I was lying in this pose, and I said to myself, *I am putting the old self to rest.*

But for many people, achieving this level of calm is difficult. And you'll have to train yourself to relax. The more you practice, the easier it becomes. And in time, it becomes a meditation. You can observe what's happening in that moment of relaxation, or you can sink into the floor and feel good just doing nothing.

When I tell people, "Relax the tiny muscles between your eyebrows, and soften your jaw," people love it. They don't realize they're clenching and creating tension. Yet thoughts are hard to control, and they come and go, keeping that tension locked into our body. *Savasana* is the chance to release and rerelease all that built-up tension.

Because relaxing and letting go is the hardest thing for many of us, it's the most important pose of all. For some, it's the most challenging because it requires nothing except lying alone with ourselves. It's full-body meditation.

Do you find that difficult? If so, return to your belly breath from Chapter 2, or try the 3D breath technique. Place your hands on the sides of your waist, thumbs wrapping around your back and fingers wrapping around your front. As you take slow, deep breaths, feel your belly and chest expand. Feel your side ribs flare as you inhale. Then feel everything deflate on your exhale. This type of slow, mindful breath calms your nervous system and trains you to use your entire lung capacity instead of accumulating tension in your upper body with short, shallow breaths.

The sympathetic system controls "fight-or-flight" responses. In other words, this system prepares the body for strenuous physical activity. The events we would expect to occur within the body to let this happen do, in fact, occur. The parasympathetic system regulates "rest and digest" functions.

Shift away from the sympathetic fight-or-flight breathing and toward the restful parasympathetic system of breath work. Over time, you'll feel it in your back, too. It's like a balloon in your torso expanding and deflating from all directions equally at the same time.

You can combine a grounding, mindful presence exercise with this breathing technique. It's done by gathering all five senses. Look around you without moving your head or neck. Take it all in—colors, textures, distance. Notice connections between the ceiling and walls. Bring the background into your foreground.

When you've had your fill of sights, close your eyes and move to your ears. Notice everything you hear. Bring background noise to the forefront of your auditory awareness. Can you hear the hum of the house? Can you hear the street and the birds outside? Can you hear yourself breathing?

Next is your sense of smell. What scents do you notice? What have you become nose blind to? Does it smell warm, salty, musty?

Now move to taste. What do you taste in your mouth at this moment? Even if you can't explain it, think about that taste and focus on it.

Last of all, move on to your sense of touch. Notice every point of contact between your body and the ground: the pressure points, the texture of the mat beneath you, the feeling of your clothes against your skin. Be aware of the air temperature and even your hair.

Tuning yourself into the present moment is practiced awareness to be here now. These techniques are calming and grounding. And they can be a good way to usher you into relaxing *shavana*, where you can just be.

Practicing *savasana* causes a shift in your state. A shift from one of movement, activity, productivity, to one of relaxation, rest, release. Your nervous system takes note, and as you settle into relaxation—grounded in the present, safe, and comfortable—you may notice you no longer feel you need to fight, flee, or freeze. You can just be. I've experienced this shift in my nervous system recently because of my trauma alchemy odyssey. It's funny because at first, I found it challenging to function without my fight-or-flight nervous system guiding me. I used to work *because* I was in fight or flight, and I would burn myself out all the time.

I had a hard time relaxing. That inability to relax resulted in health problems that forced me to see doctors and therapists. But I've now realized that because of the work I've done, much of it with ketamine, I've shifted to the parasympathetic—the rest and relax—nervous system. And I like it.

Maybe I'm not getting as much work done, but I'm relaxed about it. While I'm not as hyperproductive, I'm not stressed out anymore. I'm navigating a new world at the end of the old one.

By becoming nothing, you've become fully present. The past has died, and the future is not here yet. All that exists is this moment.

You are exactly where you need to be.

CHAPTER 12

FETAL POSITION

Y ou have sloughed off your old self like dead skin—it has died. And it felt good; now it's time for a gentle awakening. Invite small movements back into your body, and do a long body stretch as if you just woke up. Then when you're ready, roll over to one side and curl up into a fetal position. Awaken to your new self.

This position feels unfamiliar to me because I'm *not* in a constant fight-or-flight state anymore. It's like I'm a beginner again. And though I'm not getting as many tasks done, I'm working smarter, not harder, using the Pareto principle—80 percent of outcomes are derived from 20 percent of causes.

I expanded my field of vision to be more present and mindful in moments that are more fulfilling than work. There will always be more work, but there won't be more time with my family.

Now I appreciate the small moments with my children—even passing, unremarkable ones. It's like I'm taking a snapshot of each moment and appreciating it for its own sake. For instance, I think, *My son is four, walking down the stairs, and he's using the handrail; someday he'll be a big man who won't need me anymore.*

When my first child was a toddler, I was forced to slow down, and I was grateful for it. But after a while, I started to lose that gratitude. Now I've learned to step outside the moment and enjoy it. And even if past habits start to return, I'm a new person now. Those behaviors feel unfamiliar. They belong to the old me who has died: a ghost. If this happens to you, it may leave you feeling vulnerable. Take a moment to say something like, "You're not welcome here." And then turn back to the present and think, *How would I do this without that habit?*

In trauma alchemy, this step reignites your inner-child work. Your old self has died off, your inner child has been born anew, and you're moving forward in your re-parenting.

Tell your inner child, "I'll take care of you." Rinse and repeat as often as needed. That's how your adult self heals that relationship. You can observe trauma responses like fight, flight, or freeze and talk to yourself as if you're talking to a child. Most people talk to themselves in a negative manner that they would never use to address someone else. Don't you deserve the same respect?

It's OK to grieve. You might experience grief because your old self once served you, but it no longer does. And you might feel fearful to move on as your new self. You're shedding those layers and feeling raw and vulnerable. But like with any great loss, you need to move on.

It can be helpful to take a picture of your younger self and keep it on the bathroom mirror or somewhere you engage in a lot of self-talk. Speak to that inner child while you visualize and remember her. No more harsh self-criticism. That little person within you hears it, so ask, *Would I really say that to them?* If not, take a gentler tone.

Pause and let your inner child have moments of play. Let them come out as you play with LEGOs, or jump off a dock, or get muddy in some puddles. Remind them that all they need to do is play and you will maintain the healthy boundaries for them. Have patience with this reborn inner child as they navigate those boundaries. Children, after all, push boundaries just to make sure they're solid. Baby steps and patience are part of the re-parenting process.

Think of a fetus in the womb, and ask questions about their future. *Who will you be? What's your potential? How can I nurture it?*

Remember: It's never too late, whether you're thirty or sixty. We can be reborn anytime, and none of us know when we'll die.

Business magnate Bill Gates once said, "Most people overestimate what they can do in one year and underestimate what they can do in ten years." A lot can change in ten years. Or even one.

You must be born anew and not be a zombie. So we have a brief, yet mindful, transition in fetal position between *savasana* and *namaste*. Your infant self has incredible potential, and now you can reparent your inner child to change your future trajectory.

Dream as if no one could say no. You have the power to give yourself a new future, alter the course of history, stop the cycle of generational trauma, and put the past to rest. You get to have the inner childhood you always wanted. And your inner child can catch up over the next few months and years to the present moment so you can become the person you always wanted to be with the opportunities you always wanted to have.

CHAPTER 13

NAMASTE

L ook at everything that has happened prior to this point. It's time to seal it, celebrate it, and connect it with the entire world's experience. You've done the work and are ready to bring the new you into the world. You have sloughed off the trauma and released the tension, and you know your heart is open, ready to give and receive.

Namaste means "we are one," and my favorite translation explains that there is a place inside you where the entire universe dwells. That place is love, light, truth, and peace. When you're in this place in you and I am in this place in me, we are one, and there is simultaneous acceptance and recognition that we are all one. You no longer see separation between yourself and others.

The term *maya* in yoga is a veil; it's an illusion that separates you from everyone and everything else. When you say, *"Namaste,"* you lift the veil, and you recognize the inner child and divine nature in everyone—a spark, the inner source of love, light, truth, and peace.

In the SarahBethYoga community, there's no judgment, no right or wrong way. We're together in the moment, still connecting, even if you're watching a recording months or years later. It's a way to experience *namaste* in the modern day regardless of distance.

Bring this off the mat, living your *namaste*. When I had my first child, I saw the newborn child in everyone I met. The experience gave me great appreciation, compassion, and understanding for every person.

Not long ago, I saw a tweet in a similar vein from a woman with a newborn. She talked about rising in the middle of the night for feedings and changing diapers. She would think of all the women around the world who had done, were doing, or would do those things past, present, and future. That made her feel a sort of infinite sisterhood with all humanity. It made the mundane meaningful.

Most people don't see the meaning behind the mundane. They take a narrow focus on things that seem to matter but don't, like the stress of work. They feel more and more cut off from the world.

But if you step back and see a bigger picture, you realize that we're all stressing about the same things. And maybe you feel like you're the only one going through it. But in reality, there are hundreds of thousands of people—millions, even—doing that exact same thing all around the world.

That's the goal of yoga—to slip off the bonds you thought served you but are holding you back. Lift the veil from your eyes, and live in a moment of pure presence, bliss, and compassion. The physical completion of *namaste* involves bringing your hands together at heart center, bowing, and saying aloud or to yourself, *"Namaste."*

As you see the inner child of everyone around you now, you want to engage in play and create relationships with them. What do their inner children long for? What offers acceptance, love, and joy?

It's about finding the fun in little moments. When you see the inner child in someone else, you're reacting and speaking to that child. Your language will and should change as you begin to understand each person.

Now comes the preparation to get off your mat and return to life. In a literal sense, that means returning from a yoga session. In a practical sense, it's integrating your trauma alchemy practice into your day-to-day life.

CHAPTER 14

CHOICE

You've reached a point where you must ask yourself how you'll move on with the rest of your day—and your life.

And now you can choose because *everything is new.* The baggage you were carrying is gone. You've released the old, and now you can bask in this moment of renewal.

You've reached the summit, and you see the entire landscape below you. You're on a journey of growth, but remember that the journey never ends.

It's not like practicing handstands until you get it perfect. What you're doing isn't a progression of yoga; it's a progression of *self.*

Think about how far you've come on this journey with me and what drew you to this book.

We began trauma alchemy with grounding, the first pose in the sequence. Something in your life brought you to a point where you needed to stabilize yourself. You tuned out the world and took time to reflect on your past and present to begin healing.

After grounding, we began the warm-up. You started to move your body, your spine in particular, and then your limbs. These were new movements, which may have felt uncomfortable, but they were the first steps toward radical self-awareness. You began noticing patterns in your body and moving toward breaking them.

Once we warmed up, we set an intention. You learned to make it something you wanted, not what you *should* want. It went beyond gratitude or other clichés. You set priorities and examined what you wanted and needed for *you*.

We introduced the basic poses in the first flow, or Sun Salutation A. You repeated the sequence to prepare yourself for more intense poses. And you built a discipline of persistence and preparation for growth by establishing a daily routine.

In the second flow, or Sun Salutation B, we turned up the heat. You put yourself through greater challenges and adopted a Warrior Pose to take ownership of your power. Like Sun Salutation A, you repeated the sequence. But this sequence was more about challenging yourself in discomfort to grow; you went beyond the basics.

After completing the first flows, we moved on to core exercises. Holding these poses was the peak of intensity; they were humbling and strength-building. You worked on your core and your ego to face the deepest, most wounded part of yourself.

Next, we continued to Sun Salutation C, the balance poses. These longer poses required balance with little movement. Feelings of self-doubt surfaced, and intense reactions put you off-balance. But you learned that the pendulum always swings, especially when putting yourself in uncomfortable positions. You focused on doing your practice, not on being perfect.

We moved on from the intensity of the previous poses to deep stretching, hip-opening poses. These hip openers helped release pent-up emotion and correct bad posture. You forgave people and let go of relationships that didn't serve you. This step was about catharsis, which led to a more relaxed state and a lower heart rate.

After finishing the main poses of the sequence, we entered the cooldown phase. This step involved short, gentle stretches. You twisted yourself and squeezed the tension out of your body. Doing that lets you calm down, make room to reflect, and connect the dots of your life. You learned about *santosha*, being content with the present, and gratitude.

Our next step was *savasana*, or corpse pose. It was the death of your old self and the birth of a new yogi. You let yourself go into complete stillness, meditation, and observation. You became present and relaxed in full. And you learned to exist only in the present moment.

The fetal position continued what you started with *savasana*. It was a gentle awakening to your rebirth. And it ignited the next stage of your inner-child work—no more living in fight-or-flight mode. You began re-parenting yourself with this new potential as a child in the womb.

And finally, we reached *namaste*, the final step, where you found a new connection to others. You learned to open your heart and express gratitude before bringing the new you into the world. You accepted yourself and others without the illusion that you are separate from them. And you gained compassion as you recognized the inner child in yourself and everyone else. Then you got off your mat and returned to the world, hand in hand with your inner child.

Despite all you've experienced in this process, you might still feel stuck or like you're not progressing. But now you're developing inward, and you're listening to your body. You're also gaining more clarity and sharpening your skills. Your old self is gone, and your new self—your true self—is alive and well. It's just a bit raw and unfamiliar, but that doesn't mean it isn't you.

Part of your new journey involves being open to new challenges and opportunities as they come. That means other unresolved traumas *may* come up. But be careful not to go looking for them. If a new challenge presents itself, see it as a growth opportunity.

You can use this book and this flow sequence to resolve any new obstacles that come up. Just because you've gone through them doesn't mean you're perfect or done. Life presents unlimited challenges, and some won't arise until you're ready for them.

Even after my own trauma alchemy journey, I still live a human life with highs and lows, but without wild pendulum swings between dark depression and chronic anxiety and without the debilitating mood swings and outbursts I once had before. Now I feel feedback, absorb it, come back to my skills outlined in this book, and return to center.

Here's the key takeaway: Always choose levity and presence. And let go of what no longer works.

After undergoing this process, you have more compassion for yourself and others. You can now trust in the work you've done. In the meantime, go live your life. Enjoy the present, nurture your values, love your people, and make your magic moments.

Thank you for inviting me to be a part of your trauma alchemy transformation. You were made to do hard things. I hope you can see that now. It wasn't easy, but you did it. As challenges present themselves going forward, know that you can handle those, too.

Save this book as a reference or as a guide for each new season of your life. You have processed one layer of trauma, and more layers may reveal themselves now that you've gained the skills and resources to work through them. When that happens, you will know that you are fully capable, and you have this book as a tool to bring with you. Reference specific chapters as needed, or reread the entire book to do the new work.

See you on your mat.

ADDITIONAL RESOURCES

Trauma Alchemy: Transform Hardship, Stress, and Trauma into Your Best Life through Yoga may be the beginning of your inner-healing and transformation journey. Now you could be wondering where to go next. These resources may be the right step for you. This is a never-ending journey; it's an exploration of getting better and better and better. At some point, someone will tell you, "You've changed," and you'll say, "I know." The caterpillar has become the butterfly.

The Trauma Yoga Collection and Calendar

> The chapters outlined in this book have been turned into individual yoga sessions so you can supplement the work you're doing here with your yoga practice. You'll practice the strategies and techniques in real time with the poses and sequences that align so you can physically embody your healing journey. The eight-week Trauma Yoga Calendar guides you through each chapter, along with yoga practices that will give you space to contemplate and process what you've read and what it means to you. This allows you to take your time as you work through each chapter. In the end, you can revisit any specific step of your trauma alchemy by either rereading the chapter, practicing that step's yoga video again, or both.

> You can access the Trauma Yoga Collection and Calendar through the SarahBethYoga Membership + App. Go to https:// www.sarahbethyoga.com/traumacalendar to learn more.

The Grief Yoga Collection and Calendar

> Grief and loss can be traumatic. Everyone will experience or has experienced pain. Loss is as much a part of life as life itself. Yet

society turns away from grief. So when it may be time for you to process it, you may be rushed through it. This collection of grief yoga videos offers a safe place for you to process at your own pace. As you work through this collection and the associated calendar, you will experience catharsis as the grief and pain transform to love and gratitude so you can reclaim and hold space for the love you shared with the person who is gone. You can honor that connection and carry it with you into the future. They may not be here in person, but they're safe inside your heart.

You can access the Grief Yoga Collection and Calendar through the SarahBethYoga Membership + App. Go to https://www.sarahbethyoga.com/join to learn more.

The Heal Yoga Collection and Calendar

This relaxing, low-energy collection includes gently guided yoga videos for emotional, physical, and mental healing. Consider this a supplemental and supportive practice where you can calm your nervous system, stimulate digestion, and release pent-up tension.

You can access the Heal Yoga Collection and Calendar through the SarahBethYoga Membership + App. Go to https://www.sarahbethyoga.com/join to learn more.

SarahBethYoga Membership + App

Take your yoga practice to the next level with my subscription service, SarahBethYoga Membership + App, which features hundreds of exclusive yoga videos (including your favorites from YouTube), all ad-free and downloadable so you can make your yoga practice an easy part of your routine. You'll also receive dozens of daily yoga calendars to help you achieve your goals, including ones related to grief, healing, and trauma. (See related entries.) These calendars take the guesswork out of what to do and when so you can grow in your practice and into your best self. You'll also be able to access our private, loving, and supportive Facebook group, the SBY Community, where you can continue the conversation, share your practice and insights, ask questions, and communicate directly with me.

Learn more and access the SarahBethYoga Membership + App at https://www.sarahbethyoga.com/join.

YouTube

Continue applying your trauma alchemy journey to your yoga practice with one of the hundreds of free yoga videos I've created and shared on my YouTube channel at https://www.youtube.com/sarahbethyoga, where I teach over 1.6 million yogis worldwide to get fit, happy, and healthy through yoga.

Social Media

You can find me on Instagram—@sarahbethyoga—or Facebook—/sarahbethyoga—where I nurture a supportive environment for growth in both personal development and on the mat in your yoga practice. I would love to see your posts with your book and insights about your journey. Just tag me at @ sarahbethyoga.

Cognitive Behavioral Therapy

Check your health insurance network, if you're in the United States, for an in-network cognitive behavioral therapist. I recommend cognitive behavioral therapy to help you with present-day thought patterns so that you can change your behavior.

I also recommend the book *Feeling Good: The New Mood Therapy* by David D. Burns, MD. If you want to take a deep dive into cognitive behavioral therapy and learn more about how it works and why, pick up a copy today. It will catch you in your tracks as you recognize negative, unhelpful thought patterns resulting from past trauma.

Inner-Child Work

I've purchased courses from Patrick Teahan Therapy to help do my own inner-child work. Specifically, I completed "Reparenting the Inner Child," "The Children's Bill of Rights," and "Toxic Shame and Childhood Trauma." I recommend that you start with his Inner-Child Work Playlist. You can learn more about Teahan's offerings at https://www.patrickteahantherapy.com and can follow him on YouTube at Patrick Teahan LICSW.

Ketamine Infusions

Ketamine is becoming more popular—and more legal—in clinical settings and for at-home usage monitored by reputable service providers. Look up "ketamine infusion clinic near me" online and read the reviews from customers.

It is recommended that you complete a series of six infusions over the course of two to three weeks. Utilize therapy, whether ketamine-assisted psychotherapy or your own therapist, before and after each session to prepare for, process, and integrate the session's work into your daily life.

National Domestic Violence Hotline

If you are in an abusive relationship, please consider speaking with someone today. Help is available in over two hundred languages, 24–7. Call 1-800-799-7233 or text *START* to 88788.

I called a similar hotline during one of the lowest yet most transformative moments of my life. The person on the other end was warm, open, receptive, and had been where I was. If one person had made it out, I knew I could, too.

The Science of Trauma

In a 2022 episode of the *Huberman Lab* podcast, Dr. Paul Conti delves into the science- and evidence-based treatment of trauma. One of the topics covered is how to choose the right therapist and get everything you can from the therapy so you can treat trauma. You can watch the interview on YouTube here: https://www.youtube.com/watch?v=IOl28gj_RXw

Why Has Nobody Told Me This Before? by Dr. Julie Smith

This is one of the most helpful and insightful mental health books I've ever read. The author explains in straightforward, everyday language her tool kit for mental well-being. Each chapter, whether it focuses on stress, grief, mood, or motivation, will leave you asking, "Why has nobody told me this before?"

Complex PTSD: From Surviving to Thriving by Pete Walker

This has been the most insightful book I've read on the subject of complex PTSD and childhood trauma. I actively listened to this book on audible and found myself rewinding chapters just to hear them again. It is described as a comprehensive, user-friendly, self-help guide to recovering from the lingering effects of childhood trauma and I wholeheartedly agree.

ACKNOWLEDGMENTS

I'd like to thank the SarahBethYoga audience, including you dear reader, for supporting me and giving me a space to teach and grow as a yoga teacher with an affinity for inner work, mindfulness and functional movement. Your growth and desire to evolve is my biggest inspiration.

I'd also like to thank my husband Leland who loved and supported me through my own transformation from a traumatized teen to an empowered and successful woman. He saw the best in me, respected me, and encouraged me to take risks. He showed me that love doesn't include possession, manipulation or abuse. It was my husband Leland who encouraged me to go to Yoga Teacher Training over 12 years ago saying "You won't know until you try". He encouraged me to start my YouTube channel Sarah-BethYoga, he also encouraged me to launch the SarahBethYoga APP and most recently he encouraged me to write this book. His uplifting, big-picture perspective and ever-present growth mindset has given me the support I didn't know I needed to manifest my dreams, to heal, and to become the healer I always knew I wanted to be.

To my children Roman and Leo, my ultimate teachers, thank you. At the time of writing this book my boys are 6 and 4 years old. They have changed the way I live my life. They slow me down and show me the value of presence and play. When I knew I wanted to become a mother the whole world shifted and suddenly I wasn't solely living for myself anymore. I had a higher purpose: to love, live and sacrifice for these little beings whose childhoods are developing in real time, right in front of me. My inner work truly began when I became a mother and decided that the generational trauma cycle would stop with me. I'll always strive to give them what I didn't get, an emotionally-safe and secure childhood, and provide them with lessons of nervous system regulation and trauma healing so that they can thrive in the world and life ahead of them.

Lastly, I'd like to thank the SarahBethYoga team: Paige, Jason, Leland and Joshua for seeing the SBY vision and putting your time, energy and hearts into bringing this book to fruition and growing SBY to impact the world by helping people get fit, happy and healthy through yoga. I truly couldn't, and wouldn't, have done it without you.

And to all of the people I've met and will meet in this beautiful life...

My sincerest gratitude,

Sarah Beth

ABOUT THE AUTHOR

Sarah Beth is the founder of the YouTube yoga phenomenon SarahBethYoga. Over the last twelve years, she has earned more than 1.5 million subscribers thanks to her 750 yoga videos and the wildly popular SarahBethYoga App. Join other yogis transforming their health and lives on and off the mat at https://www.sarahbethyoga.com. Sarah Beth is also married and the mother of two young boys.

Made in the USA
Monee, IL
10 April 2023